basic audio

by NORMAN H. CROWHURST

VOL. 2

JOHN F. RIDER PUBLISHER, INC.
116 West 14th Street • New York 11, N. Y.

PREFACE

Audio is like Topsy: it wasn't born, it just growed. Whatever Topsy may have been like, Audio has grown like a gawky child—not always in proportion! Originally associated with radio and later with high fidelity, audio now finds application in many other places—to name a few: computors, automation, ballistics and guidance for missiles, sonar detection for navigation, ultra- and infra-sonics for medicine, both diagnostic and therapeutic, as well as geophysical and other work. In fact Audio is now one of the largest and most basic divisions of electronics.

Courses in audio were nonexistent not too many years ago. Since then, textbooks and courses have appeared. But their approach follows the principle of many professors: "I learned it the hard way—you'll have to!" It's like learning watchmaking from a bridge-building man.

My wide experience in various aspects of audio has shown the need for a better way. In industry, in academic education, and particularly in working with graduates from college, this need is evident. My extensive technical writing for magazines and consultant work in the industry have also shown me audio's educational needs.

Many competent "practical men" find themselves hindered by lack of academic background in the subject. They can do their job in their own established "groove." But they do not have—and find it impossible to acquire—the background to enable them to expand outside this groove. These people need help in closing the gap between "theory" and "practice."

Engineers are conversant with the accepted "technical language," but they read the literature with only an "intuitive comprehension" (or should it be apprehension?). Their education dragged them past many "awkward spots" about which they have never felt really "comfortable." Like the King of Siam in "The King and I," they find many facts of which they wish they were more certain they are sure.

Very important are the new students, technicians, and audiophiles. They will need a basic education in audio to enable them to add their contribution to progress (and to earn themselves a living!). Why make it difficult? They'll do much better if they can get a good start.

All-in-all, it is time that certain roundabout approaches to this key subject were eliminated. We need a direct, meaningful way to take the place of the difficult detours. Then each of our three groups can not only "learn audio," but also understand it! This three-volume book results from the author's extensive education research. The finished arrangement achieves a completely new directness.

Let me give just one example: how many understand the behavior of a coupling capacitor, particularly its contribution to amplifier transient performance, and what sometimes happens to feedback? This has always been based on the concept of capacitive reactance, which does not adequately *explain* all the effects. We have adopted a practical "what happens?" approach.

As a result, someone who learned this the old way may miss the familiar landmark of the reactance concept—when he expects it; a closer examination will reveal the reason for postponing it: the whole presentation has been arranged to avoid the "dead spots" left by the traditional approach.

Inevitably such a change of approach will mean a change of stress. I make no apology for this. I know from practice that it is far more successful in getting Basic Audio "across."

It would be impossible to acknowledge the very many who have, knowingly or unknowingly, contributed to my experience, making this book possible. But I would like to express my thanks to the John F. Rider staff for their cooperation in "packaging" it in a form that interprets my intentions so well.

NORMAN H. CROWHURST

New York, N.Y.
August 1959

CONTENTS

VOL. 2—BASIC AUDIO

The Diode

CONSTRUCTION AND ACTION OF A DIODE

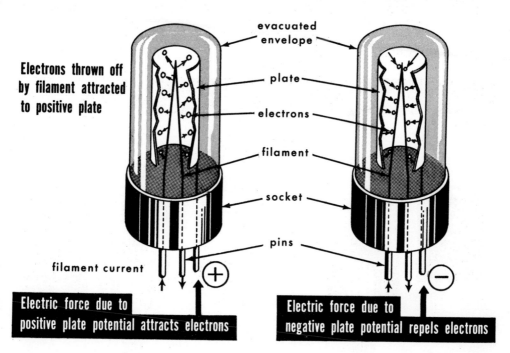

Electrons thrown off by filament attracted to positive plate

evacuated envelope

plate

electrons

filament

socket

pins

filament current

Electric force due to positive plate potential attracts electrons

Electric force due to negative plate potential repels electrons

The first electronic amplifiers used a tube type called a *triode* because it has *three* active electrodes. The earliest triodes started with an addition to the *diode (two-electrode)* tube which used a filament of wire heated by passing a current through it and a piece of cold metal called a *plate*. These elements were placed in a space from which all the air was evacuated, usually enclosed by a glass *envelope*.

The diode *rectifies* current (allows it to pass only one direction). By electron theory, this action is explained as follows: Heating the filament causes the electrons in it to become very agitated, and they leave its surface freely in a vacuum. Electrons have a negative charge, hence if a positive charge is present in the vacuum, the electrons will be drawn to it, reaching the positive electrode. If, however, the potential on the plate is negative, it will repel the electrons (like charges repel, unlike charges attract), so they will stay near the filament, and no further charge can be taken by the plate. Therefore, when the plate is negative, no charge passes, which means that no current flows through the tube.

The Triode

Whether electrons come away from the filament or stay close to it depends on the electric field at the filament surface. This force can be made negative, even though the plate is positive, by putting a negatively charged wire mesh, or grid, between the *plate* and the filament. If the grid is sufficiently negative, it will keep all the electrons close to the filament; if it is less negative, the positive force from the plate will overcome it to some extent, and some of the electrons will get through. Thus, the number of electrons that pass from the filament to the plate depends on how negative the grid is and how positive the plate is.

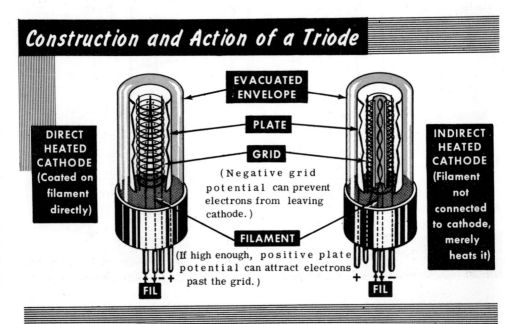

Construction and Action of a Triode

EVACUATED ENVELOPE

PLATE

GRID

(Negative grid potential can prevent electrons from leaving cathode.)

DIRECT HEATED CATHODE (Coated on filament directly)

INDIRECT HEATED CATHODE (Filament not connected to cathode, merely heats it)

FILAMENT

(If high enough, positive plate potential can attract electrons past the grid.)

FIL

FIL

Beside its modern counterpart, the early triode was crude. The filament had to have current flowing through it to keep it hot, so that electrons would be thrown off *(emitted)*. The only essential thing, however, is to have a hot metal emitter, or *cathode*. By using a separate *heater* wire, to which current is supplied to provide the heat, the cathode does not need to have this supply connected to it. This makes the tube much more versatile. Improvement in materials and better design has enabled smaller tubes to be made, and now space is further saved by putting two or more "tubes," or complete electrode assemblies, into one evacuated "envelope." (Strictly speaking, the envelope—made of glass in most cases—is the *tube*, but as each electrode assembly in one envelope *can* be used separately if desired, it has become the practice to call each assembly a "tube" because it acts as one.)

Transconductance

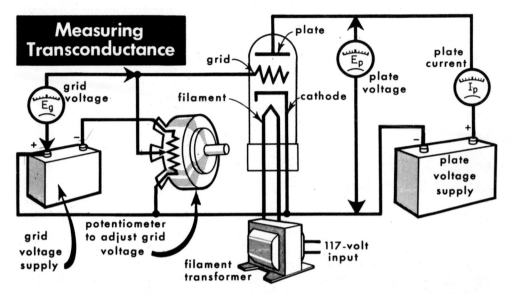

How is it that a small change in voltage at the grid can be converted into a larger one at the plate? Two things control how many electrons get away from the cathode of the tube: the plate voltage and the grid voltage. The number of electrons flowing inside the tube fixes the current in the outside circuit. Using a fixed plate voltage, the grid voltage can be changed and plate current measured each time it is changed.

Each time the grid voltage is changed, the plate current changes, until the potential on the grid is so negative that no electrons leave the plate, at which point the current becomes zero. The amount of change in plate current for each volt change in grid voltage is called the *mutual conductance* or *transconductance* of the tube. It is, of course, different for each change, but the figure usually quoted for a tube is the change that occurs when the voltage and current are nearest to the practical operating values used in a circuit.

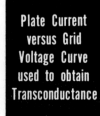

Plate Current versus Grid Voltage Curve used to obtain Transconductance

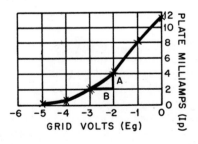

EXAMPLE:

$$\text{TRANSCONDUCTANCE} = \frac{A}{B}$$

IF Eg VARIES FROM −3 TO −2 VOLTS, Ip VARIES FROM 2 TO 4 MA

Transconductance (contd.)

Resistance is the opposition that a circuit presents to current flow—the larger the resistance, the smaller the current at the same voltage. *Conductance* is the opposite of resistance — a measure of the *ease* with which current can flow through a circuit. A higher conductance means that more current can flow at the same voltage, or that the same current will flow at a smaller voltage. *Transconductance* is a measure of the ease with which current in one circuit (the plate circuit) can be affected by the voltage in another (the grid circuit).

The relationship for resistance is the well-known *Ohm's law,* which can be expressed in symbols as $R = E/I$. The unit for conductance is the reciprocal of that for resistance: instead of being *volts per ampere,* it is *amperes per volt.* This unit is the mho (ohm spelled backwards). The conductance form of Ohm's law is $G = I/E$.

In tubes, a change of a volt at the grid only produces a change of milliamperes at the plate. (A milliampere is one-thousandth of an ampere.) For this reason, transconductance (symbolized as g_m) is generally quoted in *milliamperes per volt.* (We use g rather than G, because *conductance* applies to *direct* readings of current and voltage, whereas the tube works on *changes* in voltage and current.) Milliamperes per volt could also be called *millimhos.* But this terminology is never used; instead, the unit of transconductance is the *micromho,* which is a *microampere per volt.* (A microampere is a millionth of an ampere.) Thus, 2 *milliamperes per volt* is called 2000 *micromhos.*

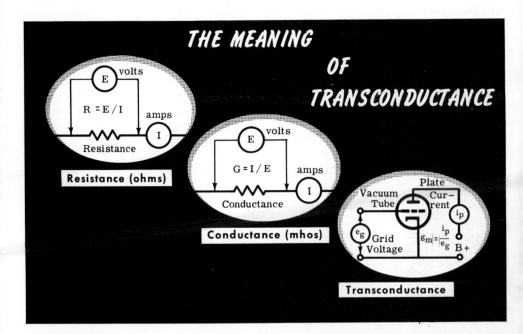

THE MEANING OF TRANSCONDUCTANCE

$R = E/I$ — Resistance — Resistance (ohms)

$G = I/E$ — Conductance — Conductance (mhos)

Vacuum Tube — Plate Current — Grid Voltage — $g_m = \left|\frac{i_p}{e_g}\right|$ — Transconductance

Dynamic Gain Measurements

In the setup we used, the plate voltage was kept constant, and a change in grid voltage caused only a change in the *current* in the plate circuit. This is not the kind of amplification needed. To be useful, a small input voltage fluctuation must give a larger output *voltage* fluctuation.

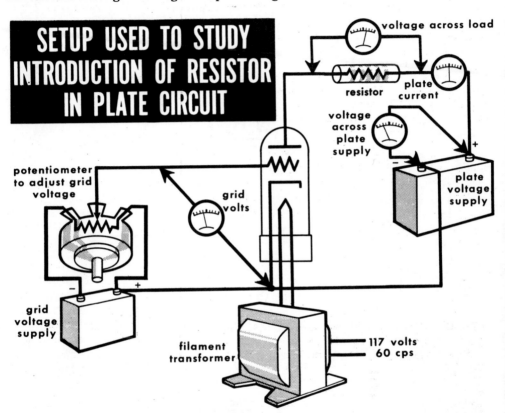

SETUP USED TO STUDY INTRODUCTION OF RESISTOR IN PLATE CIRCUIT

We can make the fluctuating plate current produce a voltage fluctuation by passing it through a resistor. The higher the value of the resistor, the greater the voltage drop that a given current will cause, and hence the greater the *voltage fluctuation* a given *current fluctuation* will produce.

The plate current, however, is dependent on *plate* voltage as well as on *grid* voltage. When the grid swings more positive (actually, *less negative*), the plate current tends to increase; but when a resistor is in series with the plate, the increased current causes the plate voltage to drop. A drop in plate voltage by itself causes a drop in plate current, hence the drop in voltage due to the resistor means that the current will not rise as much as it did for the same grid-voltage change, when the resistor was not in the circuit.

Dynamic Gain Measurements (contd.)

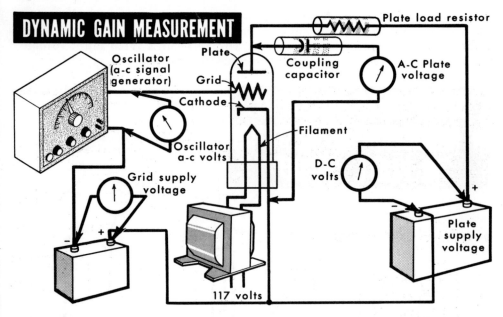

We could take a lot of time making adjustments of this kind, but there is a quicker way to get the answers we need. This is the *dynamic measuring* method. It enables us to measure the voltage fluctuation continuously, instead of having to take a whole series of individual measurements and then combine them. We apply a fixed d-c voltage, or *bias* at the grid together with a fluctuating voltage from an oscillator. (These voltages can be measured separately.) This produces a fluctuating voltage in the plate circuit that can be broken into a fixed component and an alternating component.

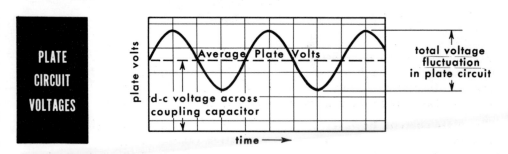

A capacitor placed between the plate and the a-c voltmeter takes on a charge corresponding to the steady or d-c component of the voltage, but does not have time to alter that charge with the alternating component. The voltmeter, therefore, measures only this alternating component.

Dynamic Gain Measurements (contd.)

Using a larger value of coupling resistor increases the output fluctuations for a given input fluctuation (the *gain* of the tube) up to a point. Eventually, the increase flattens off, and further increase in the value of the resistor causes the output voltage to decline somewhat. This decline occurs because the larger resistor values cause the *average* (steady d-c) voltage on the plate to drop, so that the tube gets "strangled." This can be overcome by adjusting the supply voltage so that the average or *operating* voltage, measured at the plate, is the same for each resistor used.

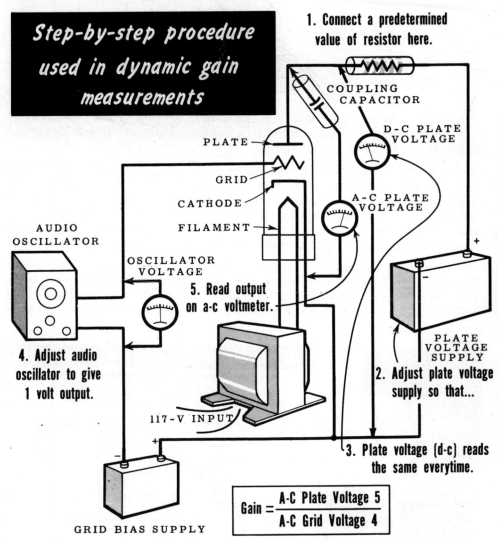

Step-by-step procedure used in dynamic gain measurements

1. Connect a predetermined value of resistor here.

COUPLING CAPACITOR

D-C PLATE VOLTAGE

PLATE

GRID

CATHODE

FILAMENT

A-C PLATE VOLTAGE

AUDIO OSCILLATOR

OSCILLATOR VOLTAGE

5. Read output on a-c voltmeter.

+

−

PLATE VOLTAGE SUPPLY

4. Adjust audio oscillator to give 1 volt output.

2. Adjust plate voltage supply so that...

117-V INPUT

3. Plate voltage (d-c) reads the same everytime.

+

−

GRID BIAS SUPPLY

$$\text{Gain} = \frac{\text{A-C Plate Voltage 5}}{\text{A-C Grid Voltage 4}}$$

Plate Resistance

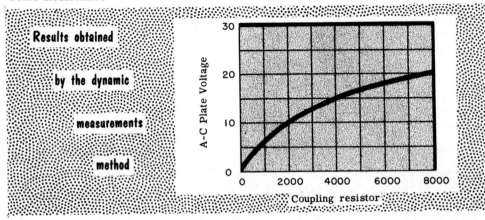

Results obtained by the dynamic measurements method

A-C Plate Voltage vs. Coupling resistor

When the tests are made this way, the output, or gain of the tube, goes up indefinitely, until we have difficulty in finding supply voltages high enough to maintain the same plate voltage.

A curve almost exactly like this can be made using only resistors without any tube. (A larger alternating voltage is needed, because there is no amplification, and the proper fixed resistance has to be chosen to get the curve the same shape.) From this we see that the tube is somewhat like a generator that produces an a-c voltage and has an *internal* resistance, the value of which is that used in the equivalent circuit that produces the same curve.

The number by which the a-c grid voltage has to be multiplied to give the input voltage in the equivalent circuit, is called the *amplification factor* (or *magnification factor)* of the tube. The value of the fixed resistor in the equivalent circuit, is called the *plate resistance* or *a-c resistance* of the tube.

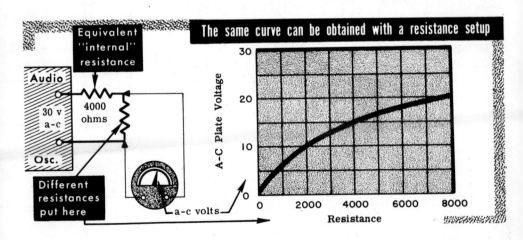

The same curve can be obtained with a resistance setup

Equivalent "internal" resistance. Audio 30 v a-c Osc. 4000 ohms. Different resistances put here. a-c volts. A-C Plate Voltage vs. Resistance

Plate Resistance (contd.)

Because voltage in a series circuit is proportional to the total resistance in the circuit, we can deduce that the output voltage from the tube is given by $\mu \times R_c / (R_p + R_c)$. The bigger the coupling resistor between the supply voltage and the plate of the tube, the less the plate *current* must fluctuate to produce a given plate *voltage* fluctuation. If, in imagination, we could make the resistance and the supply voltage infinitely large, only the plate voltage would vary. The gain of the tube in this imaginary circuit is its amplification factor.

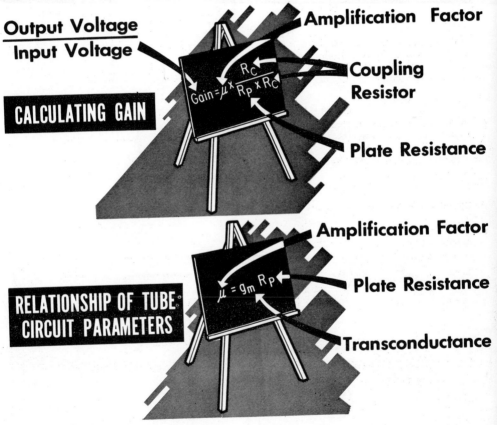

If there is no coupling resistor present (this was the case when we first examined the circuit), the voltage remains constant, and the current fluctuates. The plate current fluctuation for each volt of grid fluctuation is the transconductance of the tube. The relationship between these two conditions (which have no practical use, but help no end in figuring out the operation of practical tube circuits) is determined only by the parameter that we have called plate resistance.

ELECTRONIC AMPLIFICATION

Demonstration and Calculation of Gain

1. Set plate voltage to 250.

2. Set grid voltage to 8.5.

3. Read plate current: _10.5 milliamperes_

4. Set grid voltage to 7.5.

5. Read plate current: _12.7 milliamperes_

6. Set grid voltage to 9.5

7. Read plate current: _8.3 milliamperes_

8. Set grid voltage to 7.5.

9. Adjust plate voltage so that plate current is again 10.5 milliamperes.

10. Read plate voltage: _233 volts_

11. Set grid voltage to 8.5.

12. Adjust plate voltage so that plate current is again 10.5 milliamperes.

13. Read plate voltage: _267 volts_

14. Add 10,000-ohm resistor and oscillator.

15. Set bias to 8.5 volts, a-c input to 1 volt.

16. Set plate voltage (d-c) to 250, supply voltage reads: _355 volts_ current reads: _10.5 milliamperes_

17. Read a-c voltage output: _9.6 volts_

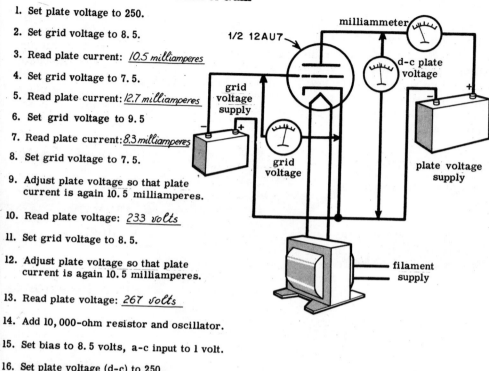

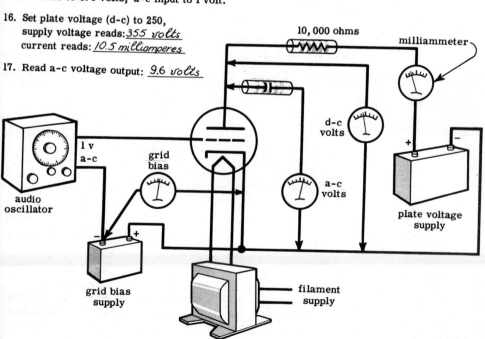

ELECTRONIC AMPLIFICATION

Demonstration and Calculation of Gain (contd.)

Let us take some figures for a real tube, the 12AU7, which is a general-purpose miniature twin triode with two sets of elements in one envelope. Since both sets have the same characteristics, we need consider only one of them. Using a 250-volt plate supply and a bias of −8.5 volts, a 1-volt change at the grid produces a 2.2-milliampere change at the plate, from 10.5 milliamperes at −8.5 volts to 12.7 milliamperes at −7.5 volts, or 8.3 milliamperes at −9.5 volts.

Of course, we cannot put the imaginary infinite resistance into the circuit, and we should have considerable trouble finding a source of infinite voltage, but we can get the desired effect by changing the grid voltage and altering the plate voltage enough to keep the plate current constant. (See steps 8 through 13.) Using this method, the current is 10.5 milliamperes with 250 volts on the plate and −8.5 volts on the grid. Changing to −7.5 volts on the grid, the plate potential must be dropped to 233 volts to keep the current at 10.5 milliamperes. Changing the grid potential to −9.5 volts, necessitates raising the plate potential to 267 volts.

From the first measurement (steps 1 through 7), the transconductance is found to be 2.2 milliamperes per volt (2200 micromhos). From the second measurement (steps 8 through 13), the amplification factor is found to be 17, because the change in plate potential required for constant plate current with a 1-volt change in grid potential is 17 volts each way. From this we can find the plate resistance (g_m must be in *amperes per volt*, to give R_p in *ohms*): therefore, $\mu = g_m R_p$ and $R_p = \mu/g_m = 17/.0022 = 7700$ ohms.

Now assume that we are using a 355-volt supply and a load resistor of 10,000 ohms, with the bias still at −8.5 volts. With 10.5 milliamperes of current passing through it, the drop will be 105 volts, still leaving the average voltage at the plate at 250 volts. By calculation, the gain should be

$$\frac{e_o}{e_i} = \mu \times \frac{R_c}{R_p + R_c} = 17 \times \frac{10,000}{7700 + 10,000} = 9.6$$

Each volt change on the grid will cause 9.6 volts change at the plate. This checks with the experiment (steps 14 through 17), using a 10,000-ohm resistor and a 335-volt supply.

With this tube, a practical amplification of about 10 can be obtained, but regardless of the way in which the tube is connected, the amplification will always be less than 17, the amplification factor of the tube.

This is the basis for calculating *voltage amplification*. The tube is regarded as producing an amplification of the input voltage, stated by its amplification factor at the chosen operating point. The actual voltage amplification is then this number, divided between the plate resistance of the tube (at the same operating point) and the plate load or coupling resistance. In the example, the total amplification of 17, theoretically provided by the tube, is divided into 7 (lost in the plate resistance) and 10 (actually delivered across the coupling resistor).

Different Types of Triodes

A great variety of tubes can be made by varying the structure of the grid and the position that it occupies relative to the cathode and plate. If the tube manufacturer winds the grid wires closer together and also puts them closer to the cathode, he will have a tube with both higher plate resistance and higher amplification factor.

Variations in structure change tube parameters

grid | cathode | plate

LOW-MU   MEDIUM-MU   HIGH-MU

CHARACTERISTICS OF TUBES

Type	Transconductance (milliamps per volt)	Plate Resistance (ohms)	Amplification Factor
12AT7	5.5	10,900	60
12AV7	2.2	7,700	17
12AV7	8.5	4,800	41
12AX7	1.6	62,500	100
12AY7	1.75	22,800	40
12BH7	3.1	5,300	16.5
ECC81	6.7	10,500	70

One-half of a 12AX7 double triode, for example, has a transconductance of 1.6 milliamps per volt, with a plate resistance of 62,500 ohms, which gives an amplification factor of 100. The transconductance is lower than that in the 12AU7 because the structure of the tube reduces the possible plate current. Tubes with a high transconductance usually have a lower plate resistance and vice versa. This fact sets a limit to the amplification that can be obtained from a single triode. What we need, to get still more amplification from a single stage, is a tube with a high transconductance and also a high plate resistance.

The Pentode

In a triode, the plate current is controlled by the combined electric field at the cathode due to both the grid and the plate. Because of the triode's open grid structure, the plate voltage influences the plate current. If we could decrease this dependence of plate current on the voltage at the plate we could boost the amplification of the tube.

This is what the pentode type tube does. Two extra grids are inserted between the number 1 or control grid and the plate. The first of these, the *screen* grid, is maintained at a constant positive potential and, from the viewpoint of plate current, is responsible for providing the electric field at the cathode. This means the control-grid voltage controls the electron flow from the cathode in conjunction with a constant field derived from the screen grid, not a fluctuating one from the plate. Because the screen grid is an open mesh and not a solid plate, most of the electrons reaching it go through the spaces instead of hitting the wires.

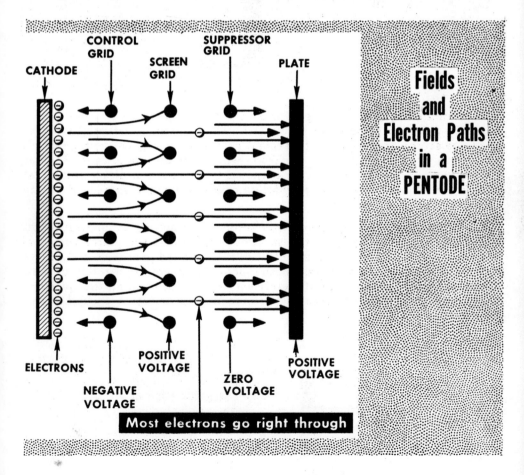

Fields and Electron Paths in a PENTODE

Most electrons go right through

The Pentode (contd.)

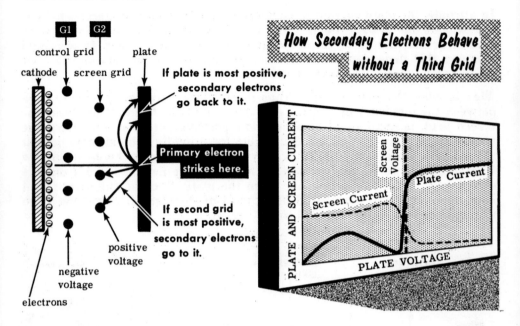

The second extra (i.e., third) grid is inserted to stop electrons from bouncing back from the plate to the screen grid when the plate potential is lower than the screen potential. If the second grid has the highest voltage of all and there were no third grid, electrons would hit the plate, cause further electrons to bounce off it, and be attracted by the more positive voltage at the screen grid. This *secondary emission* could even result in negative plate current.

The third *(suppressor)* grid prevents secondary emission by providing another electric field (between the suppressor grid and the plate) that discourages the bouncing off of any electrons. The third grid does not collect any electrons, because its voltage is so much more negative than that of both the screen grid and the plate. It merely serves to insure that all the electrons that come through the spaces in the screen grid arrive at the plate *and stay there.*

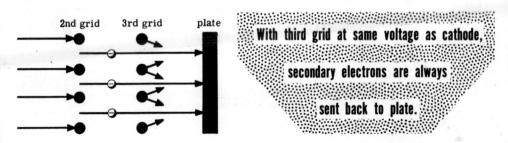

The Pentode (contd.)

This results in a tube in which the plate current is almost completely independent of the plate voltage, and is determined by the voltages on the control and screen grids. (Usually the potential on the screen grid is kept constant, and the audio fluctuations are applied to the control grid.) The plate resistance of this type of tube runs to very high values—perhaps several megohms (millions of ohms). A pentode with a transconductance of, say, 2 milliamperes per volt, and a plate resistance of 1 megohm has an amplification factor of $.002 \times 1,000,000 = 2000$.

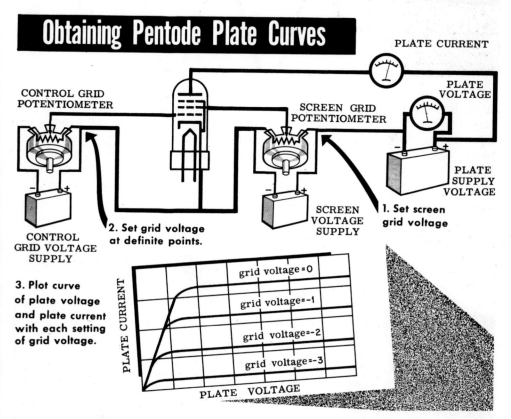

Obtaining Pentode Plate Curves

PLATE CURRENT

PLATE VOLTAGE

CONTROL GRID POTENTIOMETER

SCREEN GRID POTENTIOMETER

PLATE SUPPLY VOLTAGE

SCREEN VOLTAGE SUPPLY

1. Set screen grid voltage

CONTROL GRID VOLTAGE SUPPLY

2. Set grid voltage at definite points.

3. Plot curve of plate voltage and plate current with each setting of grid voltage.

PLATE CURRENT

grid voltage = 0

grid voltage = -1

grid voltage = -2

grid voltage = -3

PLATE VOLTAGE

This much amplification cannot be achieved in practice because a very high plate load resistor would be necessary. Supposing that we use a 1-megohm coupling resistor, using the formula we should achieve a practical amplification of 1000. As we shall see presently, even 1 megohm is rather a high value for a coupling resistor, unless we will be content with poor-quality amplification. A resistor of about 220K, however, is quite normal and will give an amplification in the region of 360, using a tube with a transconductance of 2 milliamperes per volt.

The Sine Wave

We have started to talk about alternating (or a-c) voltages, giving them figures in some cases, as we might measure them with a suitable instrument. But there are several ways of measuring alternating voltages and currents. Later on these will cause confusion if we do not get the differences straight now.

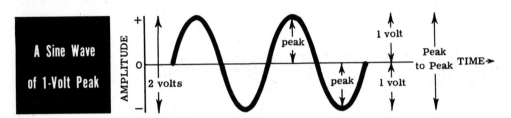

A Sine Wave of 1-Volt Peak

A pure frequency has a waveform called a *sine wave*, and is called a *sinusoidal wave*. If the wave fluctuates between +1 volt and —1 volt from 0 as the starting point, the total change, called the *peak-to-peak* voltage, is 2 volts. The "swing" each way from the central starting point is called the *peak* voltage, in this case 1 volt.

When an oscilloscope is used to observe a waveform, it is fairly easy to measure the peak, or peak-to-peak, waveform with a ruler, or by using a calibrated scale in front of the screen. Most meters however, do not measure either peak, or peak-to-peak, voltages.

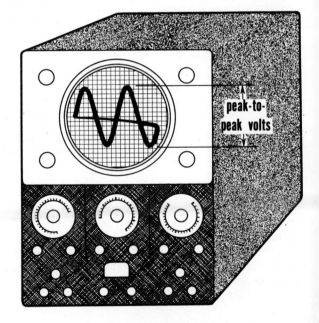

Waveforms can be measured by graph transparency on oscilloscope

peak-to-peak volts

A-C Meter Readings

If an ordinary D'Arsonval moving-coil voltmeter is connected to an alternating voltage, one half-wave will try to make it read in the normal way, while the other half-wave will try to make it read backwards, as if it had been connected the wrong way around. As the pointer will not have time to move back and forth so rapidly, it will stand still, or vibrate slightly, without moving far from the zero marking. Because of this, moving-coil meters must be used with rectifiers to get a reading.

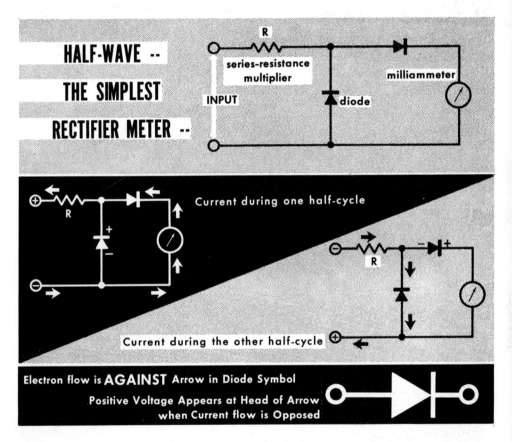

HALF-WAVE -- THE SIMPLEST RECTIFIER METER --

series-resistance multiplier

INPUT

diode

milliammeter

Current during one half-cycle

Current during the other half-cycle

Electron flow is AGAINST Arrow in Diode Symbol
Positive Voltage Appears at Head of Arrow when Current flow is Opposed

The rectifier is a metal-contact device that acts in the same fashion as a diode—it lets current flow in one direction, but not the other. In the symbol for the rectifier, the arrow points in the direction of current flow (opposite to electron flow). As a result of the action of the rectifiers, when this kind of meter is connected to an alternating voltage, one half-wave is bypassed through one rectifier, while the other half goes through the meter. Of course, the meter pointer will not have time to follow the fluctuations, so it will average out the current that flows through it.

A-C Meter Readings (contd.)

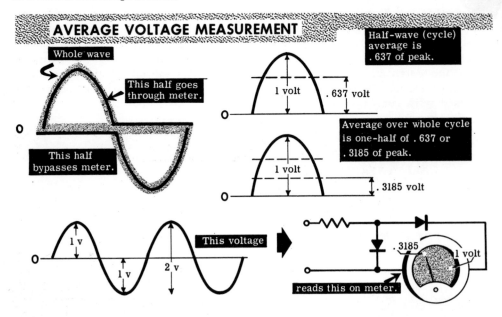

AVERAGE VOLTAGE MEASUREMENT

Whole wave

This half goes through meter.

This half bypasses meter.

Half-wave (cycle) average is .637 of peak.

1 volt — .637 volt

Average over whole cycle is one-half of .637 or .3185 of peak.

1 volt — .3185 volt

1 v — 2 v — 1 v

This voltage

.3185 — 1 volt

reads this on meter.

During one half-wave, no current flows through the meter, while during the other half-wave, it follows half a sine wave in form. The *average* of half a sine wave is 0.637 of peak value. However, during half the time, no current goes through the meter; therefore, the average over the whole time will be half of 0.637 or 0.3185. (If an ordinary d-c meter movement is used in this circuit to measure an alternating voltage, a 1-volt peak—2-volt peak-to-peak —voltage will only give a reading of 0.3185 volt.)

In an arrangement that uses four rectifiers, the meter gets both halves of the wave, and it will read 0.637 of the peak voltage if a regular d-c meter is used.

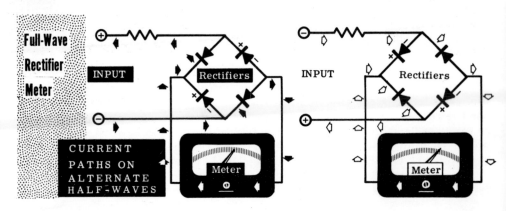

Full-Wave Rectifier Meter

INPUT — Rectifiers — Meter

INPUT — Rectifiers — Meter

CURRENT PATHS ON ALTERNATE HALF-WAVES

A-C Meter Readings (contd.)

Thus all rectifier-type meters indicate a value that is some kind of average, but the average value is not directly related to practical circuit behavior. In audio work, we must know either the maximum voltages or currents or the power ($E \times I$) associated with them. If only the level changes (impedance or resistance is constant), the power is proportional to voltage or current squared, at any instant. Average power is determined by the average (or *mean*) of the squares.

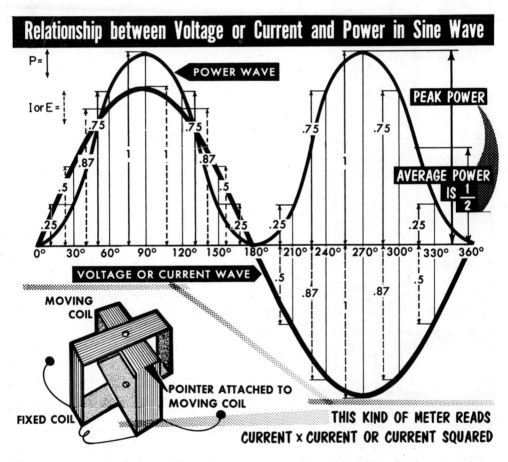

Relationship between Voltage or Current and Power in Sine Wave

THIS KIND OF METER READS CURRENT x CURRENT OR CURRENT SQUARED

The power-equivalent reading of any a-c waveform could be read on a meter where both the field and the current in the moving coil come from the circuit being measured. This is called a *dynamometer* movement. Torque at every instant is proportional to power. So, the reading will be the average *power* represented by the current or voltage. If it is marked with square-root readings, or the steady current or voltage that would give the same reading, this meter will read true *rms* of any waveform.

DIFFERENT KINDS OF METERS GIVE DIFFERENT READINGS ACCORDING TO THE WAVEFORM

Waveform	When the Actual Value is...	oscilloscope will read	half-wave meter will read	full-wave meter will read	rms meter will read
Sine	1 volt peak-to-peak	1	.1593	.3185	.3535
	1 volt peak	2	.3185	.637	.707
	1 volt rms	2.828	.45	.9	1
	1 volt average	3.142	.5	1	1.11
Triangular	1 volt peak-to-peak	1	.125	.25	.2885
	1 volt peak	2	.25	.5	.577
	1 volt rms	3.464	.4085	.817	1
	1 volt average	4	.5	1	1.224
Square	1 volt peak-to-peak	1	.25	.5	.5
	1 volt peak	2	.5	1	1
	1 volt rms	2	.5	1	1
	1 volt average	2	.5	1	1

So there are three main values related to waveforms: peak, average, and rms. To these may be added peak-to-peak (twice peak for a symmetrical waveform), and various other possibilities of averaging.

Load-Line Construction

We can find out more about amplification by plotting the curves of plate current and grid voltage with resistance connected in the plate circuit. However, we have to plot a new curve for each value of resistance with which we want to experiment. If, for some reason, we are not satisfied with any of the resistance values that we have already tried, the only thing to do is get the equipment out and plot some more curves.

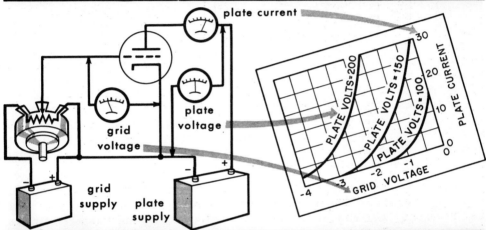

Obtaining Plate Current versus Grid Voltage Curves for various values of plate voltage, Without Plate Load Resistor

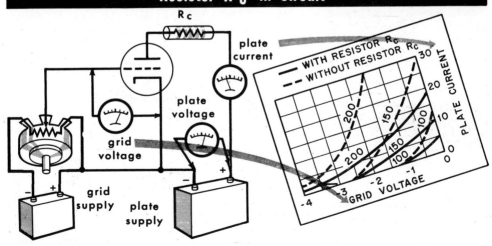

Obtaining Plate Current-Grid Voltage Curves With Plate Coupling Resistor R c in Circuit

CIRCUIT VALUES

Load-Line Construction (contd.)

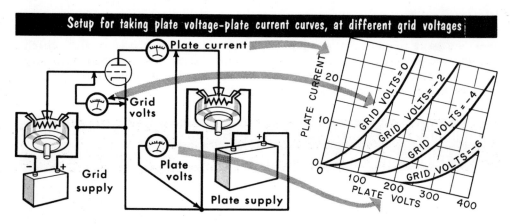

Setup for taking plate voltage-plate current curves, at different grid voltages

Fortunately there is a more direct way of obtaining all these curves. To start with we plot quite a different set of curves. Each of these curves shows all the possible combinations of plate current and voltage that can occur for one fixed potential on the grid. If we can draw, on the same graph, another line we can find all the possible relationships in the plate circuit, corresponding to whatever resistance or other circuit component is connected. Then these curves can be used to find how the circuit—any circuit—will work.

For example, if the supply voltage used is 250 volts, and the resistance used is 20,000 ohms, without any plate current flowing, the plate potential will be the same at both ends of the resistor—250 volts. If 1 milliampere of plate current flows, the drop across the resistor will be 20 volts, leaving 230 volts at the plate. With a plate current of 2 milliamperes, the drop will be 40 volts, leaving 210 volts at the plate, and so on. With 12.5 milliamperes flowing, the whole 250 volts will drop in the resistor, leaving 0 at the plate. These possibilities are shown by drawing a straight line through all these points.

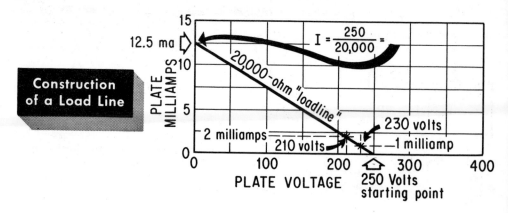

Finding the Plate Resistance

Now suppose the grid potential varies between —5 volts and —10 volts. These curves show that, when the grid potential is —5 volts, the plate current is 5 milliamps and the plate potential is 150 volts. This is where the —5-volt curve, showing possible combinations at this grid voltage, crosses the 20,000-ohm load line, showing the possible combinations with this resistor connected in series with the plate from a 250-volt supply.

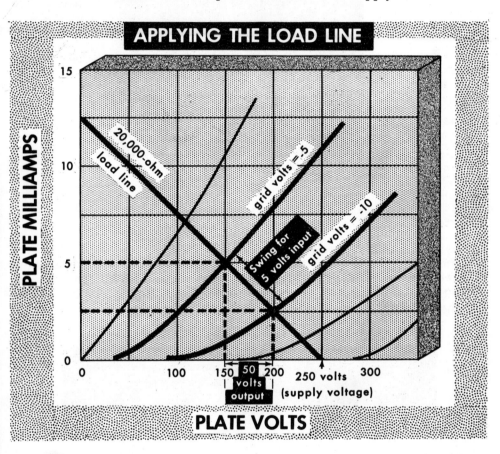

When the grid potential is —10 volts, the plate current is 2.5 milliamperes, with a plate potential of 200 volts, where the load line crosses the —10-volt curve. Thus with this resistor, we can see quite easily that there is a swing between 150 and 200 volts on the plate. If a 5-volt input swing gives a 50-volt (200 — 150) swing at the output, the tube is working at a gain of 10, because the output swing is 10 times the input swing. These curves can also be used to find the plate resistance of the tube at different operating conditions (combinations of grid potential plate current and plate potential).

Finding the Plate Resistance (contd.)

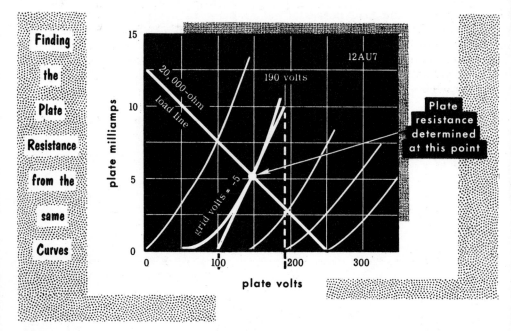

Finding the Plate Resistance from the same Curves

By laying a straight-edge (ruler) along the curve at the point where the two lines cross, its slope *at this particular point* can be found. Extending the line drawn as tangent to the curve down to the zero current line and up to the 10-milliampere line, the corresponding voltages may be read off and the plate resistance calculated.

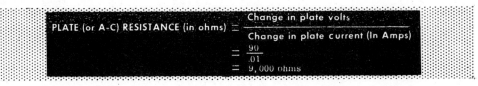

$$\text{PLATE (or A-C) RESISTANCE (in ohms)} = \frac{\text{Change in plate volts}}{\text{Change in plate current (In Amps)}}$$
$$= \frac{90}{.01}$$
$$= 9,000 \text{ ohms}$$

For example, using the 12AU7 curves and laying the ruler along the curve for —5 volts, where the 20,000-ohm load line crosses it, the line drawn as tangent goes through the zero current line at 100 volts and through the 10-milliamp line at 190 volts. This means, if the slope at the point we chose is extended, that a *change* of 10 milliamps causes a *change* of voltage of 90 volts. This is why the relationship is sometimes called an a-c resistance— because it deals with changes of fluctuations in current. The value of the resistance, in ohms, is given by Ohm's law. In this example, the plate resistance is 90/.01 or 9000 ohms.

QUESTIONS AND PROBLEMS

1. Explain why a diode rectifies current, and how the geometry of a triode affects the way in which the plate and the grid control electron flow.

2. What is transconductance, and why is it so called? State the conditions defining it.

3. What two units are used for measuring transconductance? If a tube has an amplification factor of 100 and a plate resistance of 62,500 ohms, give its transconductance in both units.

4. What is the plate resistance of a tube, and why is it sometimes called *a-c resistance?*

5. What is the amplification factor of a tube? State the conditions defining it.

6. How can the amplification of a tube be increased by its internal design? Discuss the practical limitations in achieving higher amplification from a triode tube.

7. A tube has an amplification factor of 100, a plate resistance of 80,000 ohms, and is used with a load resistor of 100,000 ohms. Calculate the approximate amplification of the stage from the appropriate formula.

8. What steps were taken in the design of tubes to obtain higher amplification than is possible with a triode? Explain the function of each added electrode.

9. Why is the amplification factor of a pentode seldom quoted in tube data for this type of tube? What figure is used instead?

10. What would happen to a moving-coil meter connected in an a-c circuit, without the use of a rectifier?

11. Draw two different types of rectifier meters commonly used for measuring a-c. State the relationship between the reading obtained and the maximum current alternations causing it.

12. Why is it that rms values are the standard used for specifying alternating voltages and currents, although most meters measure average values? How does the relationship change when different waveforms are used?

13. What two graphical ways are there of presenting the characteristics of a tube? State the relative merits of each method.

14. What is a load line? Show how it can be applied and discuss the information that may be obtained from it.

15. How can plate resistance be obtained from a tube's characteristic curves? Is plate resistance constant as various tube voltages are changed?

The Grounded-Cathode Amplifier

Thus far we have measured all voltages against the cathode of the tube. This assumes the cathode potential is zero, or in engineering language, the cathode is called the *reference* point, because everything is measured back to it. Because we also measure all potentials against the biggest reference body we can find—the earth—the part of the circuit to which everything is *referred* or measured, is called *ground,* although it may not always be literally connected to ground.

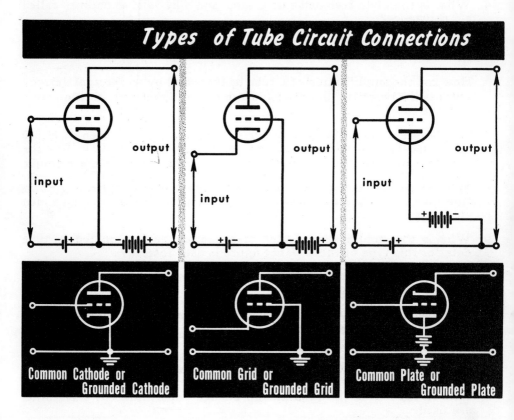

Types of Tube Circuit Connections

output

input

output

input

output

input

Common Cathode or
Grounded Cathode

Common Grid or
Grounded Grid

Common Plate or
Grounded Plate

We encounter one more expression for this: because the point to which measurements are all made is *common* to both input and output circuits, this is called a common point. The way of working a tube we have described is called *common cathode,* or *grounded cathode.*

The grounded- or common-cathode circuit of a tube is the easiest to understand because it is the voltage between plate and cathode and between grid and cathode that controls the current between plate and cathode. Any other circuit is more complicated to understand, because we have to find out how it is related to this basic one.

The Grounded-Grid Amplifier

Let us first take the grounded- or common-grid circuit. If the input voltage is applied between cathode and grid, it is the same as placing an opposite voltage between grid and cathode. (Making the grid 5 volts *negative* to the cathode is the same as making the cathode 5 volts *positive* to the grid.) No current flows in the grid circuit because it is negative with respect to the cathode and repels all electron flow. Current does flow in the cathode circuit, and it is the same current that flows in the plate circuit.

With the same resistance in the plate circuit as before and a supply of 250 volts, with a fluctuation between +5 and +10 volts at the cathode, the current will fluctuate, as in the grounded-cathode arrangement, between 5 milliamperes and 2.5 milliamperes, respectively, while the plate-to-cathode voltage fluctuates between (150—5) or 145 volts and (200—10) or 190 volts. Thus the input fluctuates between +5 volts at 5 milliamperes and +10 volts at 2.5 milliamperes, the current in each case opposing the input voltage. This means the change in input current corresponding to a 5-volt change in input voltage is 2.5 milliamperes, which represents an *a-c* resistance for the input circuit of 5/.0025 or 2000 ohms.

In the grounded-cathode arrangement, there is no current in the input circuit, hence the a-c input resistance is 5/0 or infinity. (Anything divided by zero is infinity.) Here, however, we have what in tube circuits is a low input resistance—in this example, 2000 ohms.

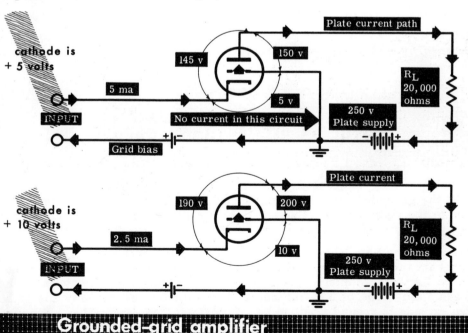

Grounded-grid amplifier

Input to the Grounded-Grid Amplifier

GROUNDED-GRID AMPLIFIER --

Input Transformer

PRI   SEC

① 5 ma
② 2.5 ma

+

① 5 volts
② 10 volts

−

20,000 ohms

−|••••••|+
250 volts

D-C resistance of secondary must be $\dfrac{7.5}{.00375} = 2000$ ohms

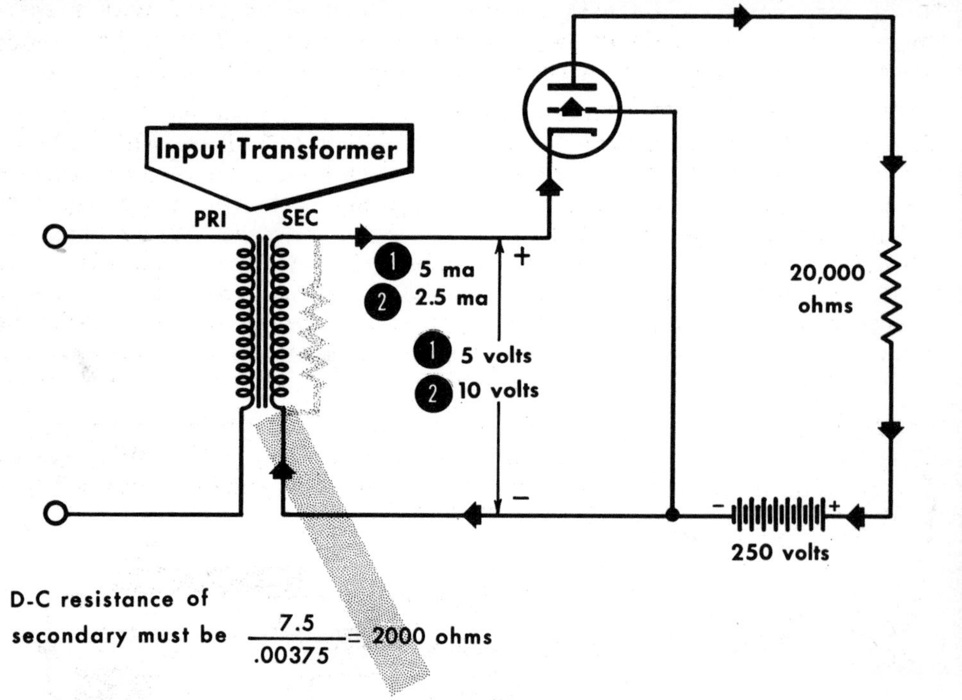

Use of an INPUT TRANSFORMER

With the grounded-cathode arrangement, the input circuit only needs to provide the right *voltage*. Current does not matter. In this circuit, however, we have to provide the right current *and* voltage fluctuations.

This is achieved by using a transformer. Assuming that the 5- and 10-volt figures are the two extremes of an alternating fluctuation, the average value will be 7.5 volts. Similarly the average current will be halfway between 2.5 and 5 milliamps, or 3.75 milliamps. Hence the d-c resistance in the path from cathode to ground needs to be 7.5/.00375 or 2000 ohms. This can be in the form of the winding resistance of the transformer secondary, or may include a separate resistor.

Input to the Grounded-Grid Amplifier (contd.)

Assuming that the transformer uses a 4:1 step-down ratio, we can work out the conditions of the input circuit. In the secondary of the transformer, there is a current that fluctuates up to 5 milliamperes and down to 2.5 milliamperes. The voltage drop due to this current (when no input is applied) is 7.5 volts. The change in voltage due to change in current will be from 10 volts (at 5 milliamperes) to 5 volts (at 2.5 milliamperes). For proper operation of the tube, however, the cathode-to-grid voltage must be +5 volts at 5 milliamperes and +10 volts at 2.5 milliamperes—just the reverse of what we have. These potentials must be provided by the induced voltage from the transformer.

Thus the induced voltage will have to offset the change in voltage drop and also provide the extra voltage for the cathode. It will have to fluctuate 5 volts each way from zero. Of this fluctuation, 2.5 volts in each direction will be taken up by the change in voltage across the secondary resistance due to change in current, and 2.5 volts will change the cathode-to-grid voltage. To produce this induced voltage on the secondary, the primary will need four times as much (or 20 volts) fluctuation each way from zero. It will also have to offset the *change* in magnetization due to the *change* in secondary current. Since this change requires 1.25 milliamperes each way on the secondary, only one-fourth of this (0.3125 milliampere) will be needed in the primary. Thus, the effective primary input must be a 20-volt fluctuation each way, accompanied by a 0.3125-milliampere fluctuation each way.

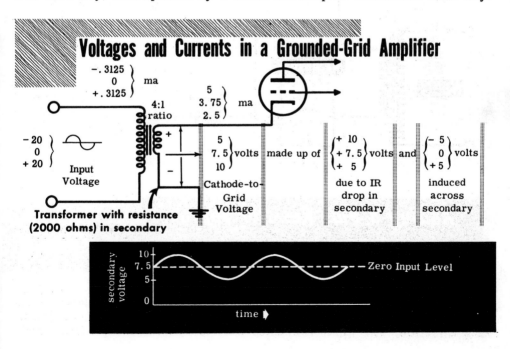

Voltages and Currents in a Grounded-Grid Amplifier

Transformer with resistance (2000 ohms) in secondary

Input to the Grounded-Grid Amplifier (contd.)

The basic grounded-grid circuit can be improved by using a separate resistor in the cathode connection to provide bias. Its value should be 2000 ohms, so that 3.75 milliamperes provide the correct middle potential of 7.5 volts. A large capacitor is connected across this resistor, so that when the current through the circuit changes, the capacitor will absorb some of it before the voltage can change. If the capacitor is big enough, the voltage will stay almost fixed at 7.5 volts.

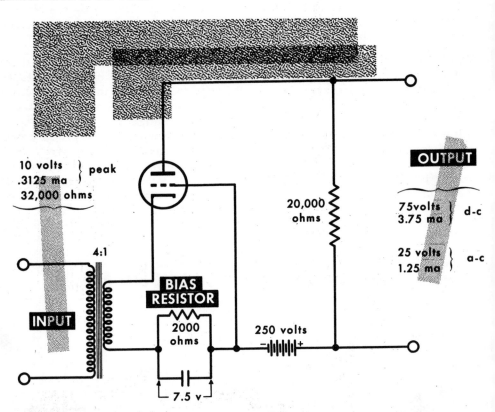

Adding a Bias Resistor improves grounded-grid amplifier circuit

This means the secondary has only to provide a voltage fluctuation of 2.5 volts each way and the primary has to receive only a 10-volt fluctuation in each direction. The input resistance thus is 10/.0003125 or 32,000 ohms.

The Cathode Follower

The Basic Common-Plate (Cathode Follower) Circuit

5 volts
10 volts

250 v — Plate Supply

INPUT

R_K
20,000 ohms

OUTPUT

95
40 volts (no current)

100 volts 5 ma
50 volts 2.5 ma

55-volt fluctuation

50-volt 2.5-ma fluctuation

The third way to connect a tube makes the plate common. We do this by connecting the 20,000-ohm resistor in the cathode circuit. Now the change of —5 volts to —10 volts between grid and *cathode* results, as before, in a change in current through the tube between plate and cathode, from 10 milliamperes to 5 milliamperes. Thus the cathode will fluctuate between 100 volts and 50 volts, respectively, due to the different currents flowing in the 20,000 resistor.

Adding these voltages together, we can find what input voltages we have to use to get these output voltages. With —5 volts between grid and *cathode,* the voltage from cathode to ground is 100 volts, so the voltage from grid to *ground* must be (100—5) or 95 volts. With —10 volts from grid to *cathode,* the cathode to ground voltage is 50 volts, hence the grid to *ground* voltage must be (50—10) or 40 volts. Thus, this circuit requires an input fluctuation between 95 and 40 volts (55 volts) to get an output fluctuation of only 50 volts, between 50 and 100. How can this be amplification?

The answer is that the cathode follower does not give *voltage* amplification. Because the grid input does not require any current to cause the output circuit to give a current fluctuation of 5 milliamperes, we can see that this arrangement can be regarded as a *current* amplifier. Because the output voltage at the cathode is almost the same as the input voltage at the grid (although more current fluctuation is available at this voltage), this circuit is called a *cathode-follower,* the idea being that the cathode voltage *follows* the grid voltage.

Transistor Operation

Tubes are not the only devices used for amplification. *Transistors* use an entirely different principle. We could epitomize the operation of a tube by saying that the plate and grid voltages combine to control the plate-to-cathode current. Or alternatively, in a given arrangement, the grid voltage controls the voltage and current in the plate-to-cathode circuit. In a transistor, it is the *current* in the circuit between *emitter* and *base* that controls the voltage and current between *collector* and *base*.

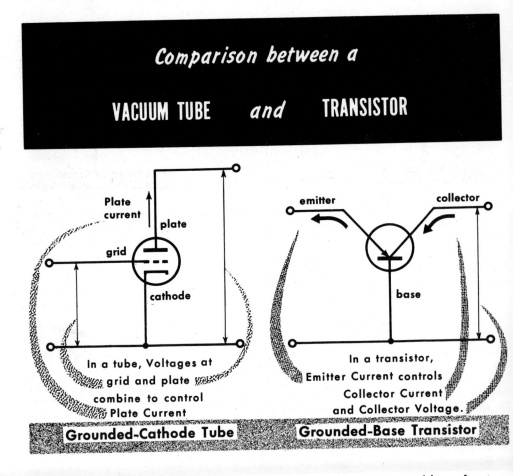

Comparison between a

VACUUM TUBE *and* TRANSISTOR

In a tube, Voltages at grid and plate combine to control Plate Current

Grounded-Cathode Tube

In a transistor, Emitter Current controls Collector Current and Collector Voltage.

Grounded-Base Transistor

To understand what all this means, we need to know something about a transistor. It is essentially a piece of special alloy, using germanium or silicon as a base, with very small amounts (a few parts in a million, very accurately controlled) of an "impurity" added. Two electrodes are connected to this carefully blended base. They may be point contact "whiskers" or a "grown junction," formed by a process called electrolytic deposition.

Transistor Operation (contd.)

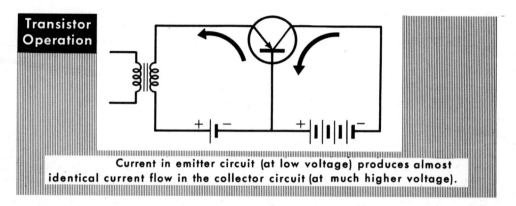

Transistor Operation

Current in emitter circuit (at low voltage) produces almost identical current flow in the collector circuit (at much higher voltage).

However it is made, the transistor works by having a potential applied to the electrode called the *collector* in the direction *against* the normal flow of current for this kind of device. (Either of the junctions between the electrodes and the base would act as a rectifier allowing current to flow one way but not the other).

Until the *emitter* circuit has current flowing in it, the current in the collector will be very small—almost zero. When current is drawn through the emitter in the direction of easy flow, however, it allows an almost equal flow of current between collector and base, so the total current flowing in the base circuit is quite small compared to the other currents in the circuit. This action can be regarded as the emitter supplying the base with surplus electrons, which the collector can then draw off. The collector current is dependent on the emitter current. It is, of course, also dependent on the collector voltage; if there were no voltage on the collector, no current would flow in the collector circuit.

Amplification is achieved, as in the tube circuit, by connecting a resistor in the collector circuit, so the changes in collector current (which follow the changes in emitter current) produce fluctuations in collector *voltage*. We can, therefore, make an amplifier by having the current in the emitter circuit control the current *and voltage* in the collector circuit.

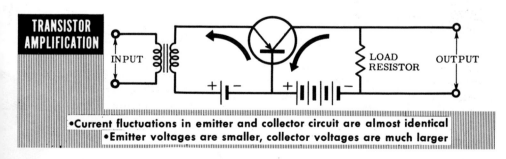

TRANSISTOR AMPLIFICATION

INPUT

LOAD RESISTOR

OUTPUT

•Current fluctuations in emitter and collector circuit are almost identical
•Emitter voltages are smaller, collector voltages are much larger

The Grounded-Base Amplifier

The grounded-base transistor amplifier is very like the grounded-grid vacuum-tube amplifier. In the vacuum-tube amplifier there is no current in the grid connection to ground. In the transistor amplifier, this current is small compared to that in the emitter and collector connections. In addition, only small voltages are needed to cause the necessary current fluctuations in the emitter circuit, whereas (by using a higher voltage and a high resistance in the collector connection) much higher voltages can be obtained at the collector.

This gives us a clue to how the transistor can be used to amplify. If the grounded-grid amplifier is like the grounded-base transistor, we should find that the tube grid is like the base of a transistor, the cathode like the emitter (they even sound similar, because a cathode is used to *emit* electrons), and we must always remember that *voltages* control electron flow in a tube, whereas currents (or electron distribution) control voltage and current effects in a transistor.

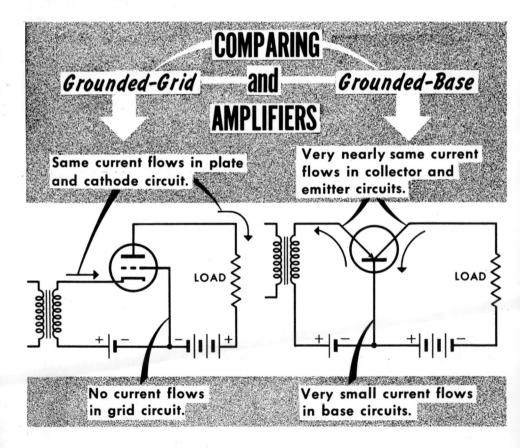

The Grounded-Emitter Amplifier

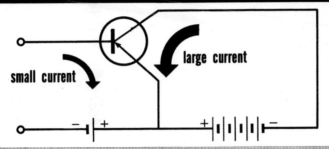

GROUNDED-EMITTER AMPLIFIER WITH NO LOAD

small current

large current

A small current and voltage change in the base circuit produces a much larger Current Change in the collector circuit.

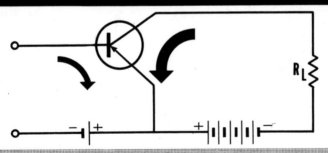

GROUNDED-EMITTER AMPLIFIER WITH ADDED LOAD RESISTOR R$_L$

R_L

A small voltage and current change in the base circuit produces a much larger Voltage and Current Change in the collector circuit.

By turning the circuit around to what is called *grounded-emitter* connection, the input is applied to the base. Only a small proportion of the emitter current flows through the base connection. With a transistor, the current applied to the base is more important than the voltage. Because of the small size of the base current compared to the collector current, this circuit can be regarded as providing current amplification. In addition, voltage amplification can be obtained by using a resistor in the collector circuit.

The Grounded-Collector Amplifier

The remaining possibility for connection of a transistor—grounded collector—is very like the cathode-follower connection of a vacuum tube. In this arrangement, the voltage between base and emitter is small because it is in the direction of easy current flow. The collector-circuit resistor is connected in the emitter circuit, hence the collector-emitter current fluctuations pass through it, causing an output voltage between the emitter and ground. Because the base is used for the input connection, both the a-c and d-c components of the input current are much smaller than in the output current.

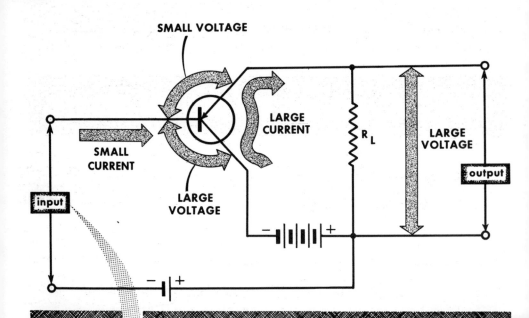

Grounded-Collector Amplifier

SMALL VOLTAGE

LARGE CURRENT

R_L

LARGE VOLTAGE

SMALL CURRENT

LARGE VOLTAGE

input

output

A large voltage and small current control almost the same voltage at much larger current

A-C and D-C Components

Thus far we have shown how smaller voltage or current fluctuations can, by using tubes or transistors, cause bigger voltage or current fluctuations. This is the essence of amplification, but one thing more is necessary to be able to make use of amplification.

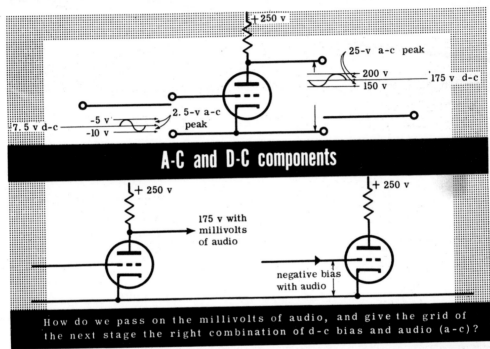

A-C and D-C components

How do we pass on the millivolts of audio, and give the grid of the next stage the right combination of d-c bias and audio (a-c)?

In the first practical amplifier stage discussed, an input fluctuation of 5 volts at the grid produced an output fluctuation of 50 volts at the plate. We did not pay much attention to the fact that these fluctuations do not conveniently start from zero or the negative bias required by the grid of a following stage. The grid circuit fluctuation could be regarded as being 2.5 volts away from an average (d-c) bias of 7.5 volts. The plate output is a fluctuation of 25 volts each way from an average (d-c) component of 175 volts.

This would, of course, run in proportion. If we start from a microphone, the voltage fluctuations will only be measured in millivolts, or thousandths of a volt. The first stage of amplification would raise this to tens of millivolts—still a rather small signal that would require more amplification to make it useful.

The easiest way to eliminate the d-c components in the output is to use a capacitor. Current does not flow from one plate to the other of a coupling capacitor, but current can flow to the plates, producing a charge on them, accompanied by a difference in voltage between them.

Coupling Capacitors

In the absence of fluctuations (audio), the plate or foil of the capacitor connected to the grid resistor takes the grid bias voltage. If there is any charge that would produce a different voltage, it flows away through the resistor, so that the voltage is again equalized. The same thing happens at the foil connected to the plate of the previous tube— it is at the same voltage as the tube's plate.

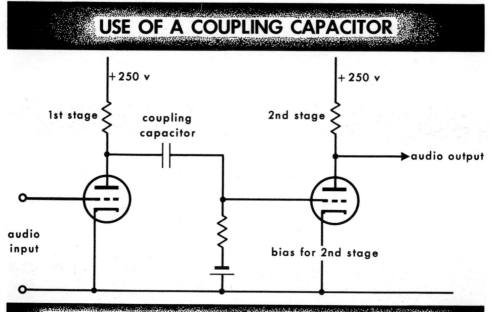

USE OF A COUPLING CAPACITOR

The COUPLING CAPACITOR prevents the d-c voltage from reaching the grid of the next stage while passing on the audio fluctuations

When audio signals come along, the voltage at the plate goes up and down from its steady resting point. Because the grid resistor is so large, the charge on the capacitor does not have time to change, hence the voltage across the capacitor does not change. This means the voltage at the grid fluctuates up and down from its steady voltage in exactly the same way as the previous tube plate. (The capacitor acts as a short-circuit for the fluctuations, while isolating the d-c components at plate and grid.) If the voltage at the previous tube plate changed permanently, the charge on the capacitor would also change, so that the potential on the grid side would be the same as ground potential, while that at the plate side assumed the new plate potential. This process (as we have shown) takes a time dependent on the size (value) of the capacitor.

Time Constants

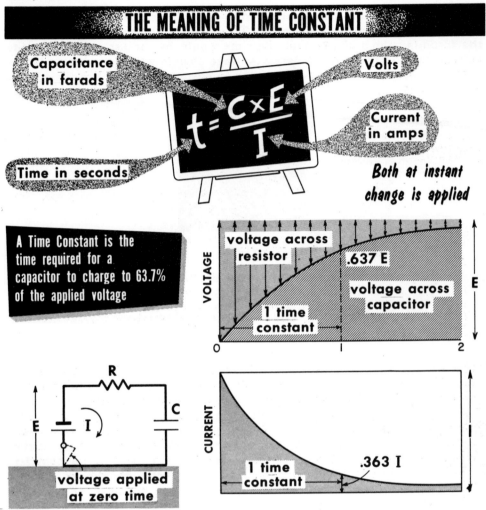

THE MEANING OF TIME CONSTANT

Capacitance in farads

Volts

$$t = \frac{C \times E}{I}$$

Current in amps

Time in seconds

Both at instant change is applied

A Time Constant is the time required for a capacitor to charge to 63.7% of the applied voltage

voltage across resistor

.637 E

voltage across capacitor

1 time constant

VOLTAGE

E

R

C

E

I

voltage applied at zero time

CURRENT

1 time constant

.363 I

I

To understand the way in which a coupling capacitor operates, we need to know about time constants. When the voltage between the terminals of a resistance-capacitance combination (such as the coupling capacitor and grid resistor) changes, the charge across the capacitor does not change immediately. Therefore the voltage across the capacitor is initially the same as before the change. Current immediately *starts* to flow in the resistor, because all the change in voltage appears across it. This will determine the initial current according to I=E/R. If a current of this size continued to flow, it would take a certain time to change the charge on the capacitor, equalizing the voltage across it. In seconds, the time would be given by $t = C \times E/I$.

Time Constants (contd.)

Because the current is also determined by the voltage change, E, that started it, the time can be written as t = RC. This now eliminates both E and I from the formula, which shows that the time would be the same whatever the voltage change involved. (A larger voltage change would produce a larger current, hence the time for the charge to change would be the same.)

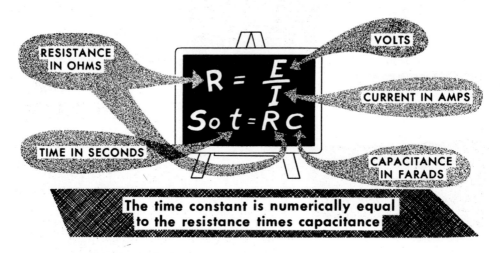

RESISTANCE IN OHMS

VOLTS

CURRENT IN AMPS

TIME IN SECONDS

CAPACITANCE IN FARADS

$$R = \frac{E}{I}$$
$$So \; t = RC$$

The time constant is numerically equal to the resistance times capacitance

However, the current does not remain constant until the voltage equalizes, and then stops. The flowing of current causes a rise in the voltage across the capacitor and a corresponding fall in the voltage across the resistor. This, in turn, causes the current in the resistor to decrease. The current thus drops off gradually before the change in voltage is complete. In fact, in the time it would take to make the whole change if the starting current were maintained, the change actually reaches only 0.637 of its complete change. In theory it never does quite reach the complete change, because the current keeps falling off indefinitely, and so does the voltage difference.

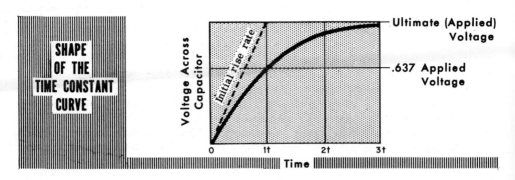

SHAPE OF THE TIME CONSTANT CURVE

Voltage Across Capacitor

Initial rise rate

Ultimate (Applied) Voltage

.637 Applied Voltage

0   1t   2t   3t

Time

R-C Coupling

At higher frequencies, the charge on the capacitor hardly changes at all during an audio-frequency fluctuation. At low frequencies, however, there is time for the charge to change, which changes the voltage across the capacitor. If the frequency is low enough, the voltage across the capacitor changes as much as the plate potential, and the potential of the grid of the second tube hardly changes at all. At intermediate frequencies, the voltage at the second-stage grid fluctuates by an intermediate amount.

At the higher frequencies, the current through the grid resistor, due to the audio fluctuations, is the same as if the resistor were connected directly to the plate, without the steady d-c voltage difference being there. Where does this audio current come from? The plate circuit of the tube has to supply it. When the plate fluctuates negative, due to momentarily greater current through the coupling resistor, the grid of the following stage goes negative as the result of current flow through the grid resistor from grid to ground, adding to the momentary plate current. We use the term *coupling resistor* for the component that feeds B plus to the plate. Some call it the *plate resistor,* which must be carefully distinguished from plate resistance. Many call it the *load* resistor, which can be misleading. As we have just seen, current fluctuations related to stage amplification divide between this resistor and the grid resistor coupled to it by the coupling capacitor. So, at most frequencies, the *load* for the tube's plate is these two resistors effectively in parallel. We will call this the *load resistance.*

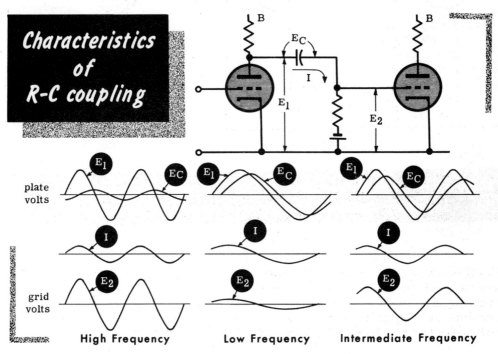

High Frequency   **Low Frequency**   **Intermediate Frequency**

R-C Coupling (contd.)

Because this increase in plate current is controlled by the voltage applied to the grid, this extra current means that the rise in current *through the coupling resistor* will not be so great as before the capacitor and grid resistor were connected. The effect is the same as if the grid resistor were connected in parallel with the load resistor.

Taking Audio Fluctuations from the Plate Circuit

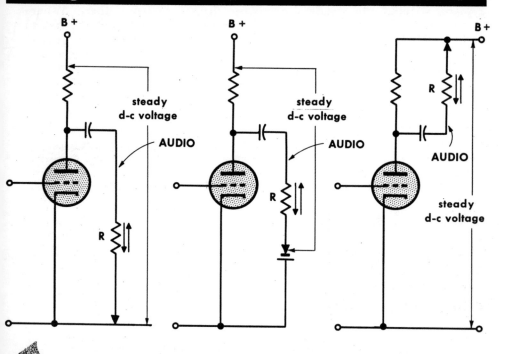

No matter where the other end of resistor R is connected, it takes the same current and voltage fluctuations from the plate

Whether the resistor to which the output side of the capacitor is connected goes to ground or to B+ will only make a difference to the charge on the capacitor and the steady voltage across it. The *fluctuations* across the capacitor and the audio currents will be the same either way because B+ is always a fixed voltage difference from the ground.

Constructing The New Load Line

We can apply these facts to the load line. The actual load resistor connected between B+ and the plate controls the steady operating point, according to the steady grid bias voltage. This operating point is found by using the load line corresponding to the coupling resistor, starting from the B+ voltage used.

Audio fluctuations cause the plate current and voltage to fluctuate in a manner that can be indicated by drawing a load line through the operating point, at a slope representing the combined resistances of the coupling resistor and grid resistor in parallel.

In the example we used before, the plate coupling resistor was 20,000 ohms. If we use a grid resistor of 100,000 ohms, the *effective* resistance of these two working in parallel for (audio only) is (20,000 × 100,000)/(20,000 + 100,000) or 16,670 ohms. Drawing a line representing this resistance, through the 175-volt/3.75-milliampere operating point, can be achieved as follows: three milliamps through 16,670 ohms will produce a voltage drop across it of 50 volts. Hence 6.75 milliamps on this load line will correspond with 175—50 or 125 volts.

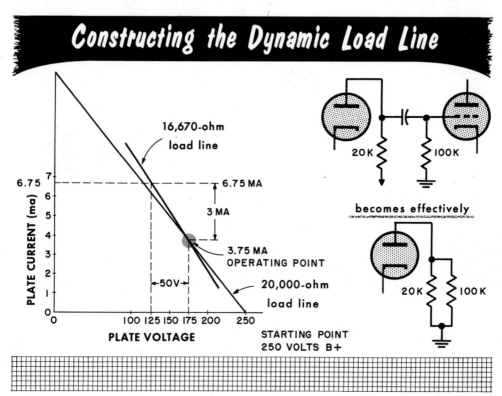

Constructing the Dynamic Load Line

16,670-ohm load line

6.75 MA

3 MA

3.75 MA OPERATING POINT

50V

20,000-ohm load line

PLATE CURRENT (ma)

PLATE VOLTAGE

20K 100K

becomes effectively

20K 100K

STARTING POINT
250 VOLTS B+

Constructing The New Load Line (contd.)

THE COMPLETE DYNAMIC LOAD LINE

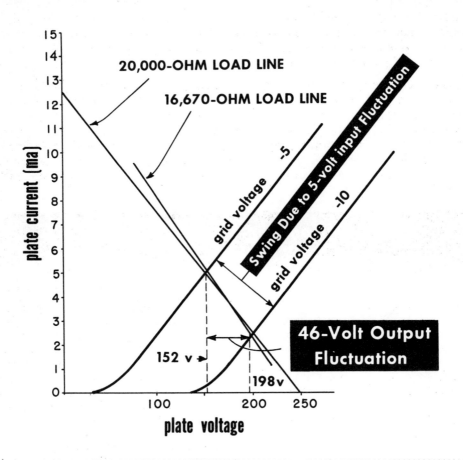

Joining these points and extending the line we can find the new values of plate voltage corresponding to fluctuation of grid voltage between —5 and —10. The new voltages, instead of 150 and 200, as on the 20,000-ohm load line, are now 152 and 198 volts. Thus a 5-volt input fluctuation yields a 46-volt output fluctuation. The gain is 46/5 or 9.2, instead of the 10 obtained before.

Direct Coupling

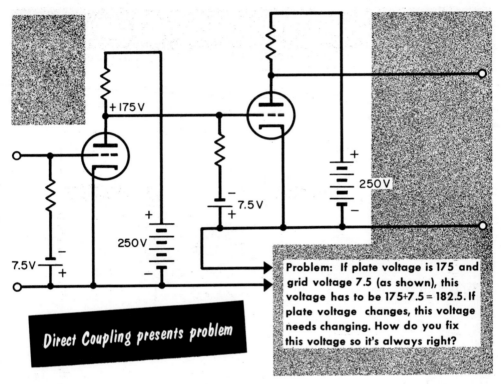

+175 V

7.5 V

250 V

+

250 V

250V

7.5V

Direct Coupling presents problem

Problem: If plate voltage is 175 and grid voltage 7.5 (as shown), this voltage has to be 175+7.5 = 182.5. If plate voltage changes, this voltage needs changing. How do you fix this voltage so it's always right?

An alternative to resistance-capacitance coupling is direct coupling. This system requires several separate supply voltages, however, and there is a problem in getting them all set—and maintained—at their right values. For example, if the working plate voltage of the first tube is 175 volts and the next stage needs 7.5 volts bias, the second-stage cathode must be exactly $175 + 7.5 = 182.5$ volts positive from the first-stage cathode. This voltage must be maintained in addition to the *voltage supplies* needed to provide plate current.

If the plate voltage should happen to be 170 volts and the second cathode is still positive 182.5 volts, its bias will become 12.5 volts, which is too much. When more stages are added to this system, a very small error in voltage at the input end can result in later stages being biased completely out of operation.

The problem then is that a number of supplies are needed, and they have to be very accurately controlled to the right value—which may vary with room temperature or a number of other things.

Such designs have been developed for computor applications, which are not audio and therefore will not be discussed here.

Direct Coupling (contd.)

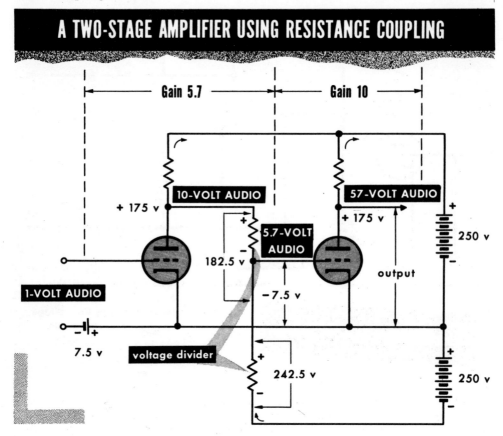

A TWO-STAGE AMPLIFIER USING RESISTANCE COUPLING

Another system that uses resistance coupling has just two supplies, one positive and one negative. To bring the voltage at one plate down to a suitable level for the following grid, two resistors are used as a voltage divider. Of course these resistors will divide the available fluctuation at the plate as well as dropping the steady voltage.

Suppose the gain of the previous stage is 10 (as calculated at first), and the plate potential is 175 volts. If the negative supply is 250 volts, like the positive supply, the resistors that give the correct steady voltage for the following grid must give —7.5 volts at their junction, or be in the ratio of 182.5 : 242.5. The fluctuations will be divided by $(182.5 + 242.5)/242.5 = 1.75$. The gain from the grid of the first stage is now 10/1.75 or 5.7, being first multiplied by 10 in the tube, then divided by 1.75 in the resistance coupling. Resistance-capacitance coupling gives better results than direct coupling. Its main disadvantage is that it ceases to be effective at some low frequencies, fixed by the time constant of the resistor-capacitor combination.

QUESTIONS AND PROBLEMS

1. Why is grounded-cathode operation referred to in this book as the basic method of connecting a tube?

2. How does a grounded-grid amplifier differ from a grounded-cathode amplifier? Does the load resistance in the plate circuit affect the performance of either circuit?

3. Why is it advantageous to bypass the bias resistor in a grounded-grid amplifier? Illustrate with numerical example.

4. What is a cathode follower, and why is it so called? Explain how the cathode follower provides a form of amplification.

5. A certain tube, operated at a grid bias of −1 volt, with a plate load resistor of 220,000 ohms, has a gain of 60. Calculate (a) its input resistance, operated grounded grid, and (b) its voltage gain, operated as a cathode follower.

6. Compare the essential control properties of a tube and transistor. What would you regard as the basic mode of operating each of them?

7. How can a transistor be operated to give characteristics very similar to a tube; with what essential difference?

8. Why is some form of coupling circuit necessary in an amplifier using two or more stages? What is the most common form of coupling?

9. How would you explain the concept of the *time constant?* Why is it not the full time taken for a capacitor to reach its final charge?

10. What properties of amplifier circuits in general are responsible for (a) low-frequency response, (b) high-frequency response?

11. How does an a-c load line differ from a d-c load line? A tube with a plate resistance of 60,000 ohms using a load resistor of 120,000 ohms gives a gain of 54. Calculate (a) its amplification factor; (b) its gain when coupled by a capacitor to an additional resistance of 200,000 ohms.

12. What is direct coupling? Describe two possible ways of using it.

Problems of Amplification

To make up an amplifier we have to see that each tube, or stage of amplification, can handle the audio fluctuations expected of it. We saw earlier that there is a limit to the maximum voltages an amplifier can handle. This is particularly important towards the later (output) stages of an amplifier. (At each stage the audio voltages are larger than at the previous stage, so the biggest audio voltages are encountered near the output end.)

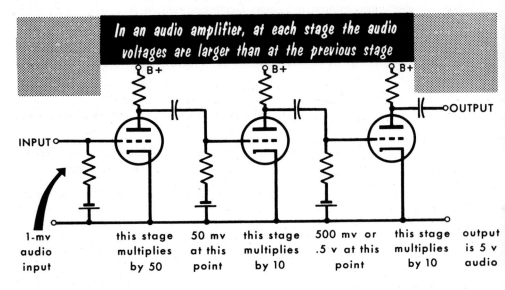

1-mv audio input	this stage multiplies by 50	50 mv at this point	this stage multiplies by 10	500 mv or .5 v at this point	this stage multiplies by 10	output is 5 v audio

There is also a limit to how *small* a voltage can be amplified. This is because of *noise*. In any circuit, even when there is not supposed to be any signal (audio), the natural electronic agitation going on in all matter causes a basic random fluctuation, called noise. According to physical theory, every molecule of matter is in a stage of agitation, the amount of which depends on its temperature. As we do not operate electronic equipment in a temperature of absolute zero (—273°C) we always have this agitation to contend with.

In every amplifier circuit, various kinds of noise set a lower limit to the audio voltages that can be successfully amplified. If the noise produces, say 2 microvolts (2 millionths of a volt), then audio voltages lower than this will get "lost" in the noise. In fact a good margin *above* the noise should be available for quality reproduction.

If, at a certain stage in an amplifier, the noise level is 2 microvolts and the maximum level before the amplifier distorts the waveform is 2 volts, the *dynamic range* or the ratio between maximum and minimum levels that can be handled is 1,000,000 to 1, or 120 decibels. (1,000,000 to 1 in voltage or current ratio is equivalent to 1,000,000,000,000 to 1 *power* ratio.)

Noise and Dynamic Range (contd.)

MAXIMUM AND MINIMUM LEVELS OF DISTORTION AND NOISE

Noise level	1μv	5μv	10μv	50μv
Distortion level	300 mv	2 v	5 v	50 v
Dynamic range of stage	110 db	112 db	114 db	120 db
Lowest audio	1μv	50μv	500μv	5 mv
Highest audio	10 mv	500 mv	5 v	50 v
Margin over noise	0	20 db	34 db	40 db
Margin below distortion	30 db	12 db	0	0

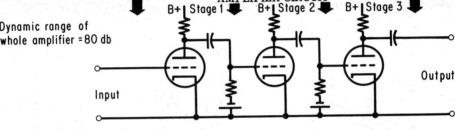

AMPLIFIER CIRCUIT

Dynamic range of whole amplifier = 80 db

Each stage of an amplifier will have its own maximum and minimum levels, fixed by distortion and noise, respectively. Each stage will have different limits. Also, the audio level corresponding to maximum and minimum through the whole amplifier will be different. For example, a three-stage amplifier may have successive voltage amplifications of 50, 10, and 10, making a total amplification of 5000. At each place from input of the first stage to output of the last stage, there will be a point at which distortion would start and a level of noise *for that circuit.* In short, each stage will have its own dynamic range, which may vary from stage to stage, but will be more than 100 db at each point.

But if we start at the lowest level, the noise level, of the first stage and amplify up (say it is 1 microvolt), the output will be a minimum of 5 milli-volts (mv), although the noise level for that stage is only 50 microvolts (μv). Due to the amplification, each stage progressively gets a bigger margin above the noise level, for lowest audio amplified.

Now if we start at the maximum level for distortion at the output—say, 50 volts—and work backward, we find this needs an input of 10 mv, although the first stage will accept 300 mv before distortion. As we work back from the output, we find a bigger margin between the maximum audio signal in the amplifier as a whole and the maximum for that stage.

So, although each stage by itself has a dynamic range of more than 100 db (the lowest is 110), the whole amplifier is limited by the distortion of the output stage and the noise of the input stage. The ratio between lowest and highest audio in the amplifier as a whole is 10,000:1, or 80 db. In a very high gain amplifier, an overall dynamic range of 60 db would be good.

Sources of Noise

Anything that is in an electrical circuit can be a source of noise. In most components the effective noise is in some way related to their *resistance*. A resistor, regardless of its dimensions, produces a certain noise energy, dependent on its temperature. Any resistance produces noise in this way— the resistance of transformer windings, of the coils in microphones and pickups, and so on.

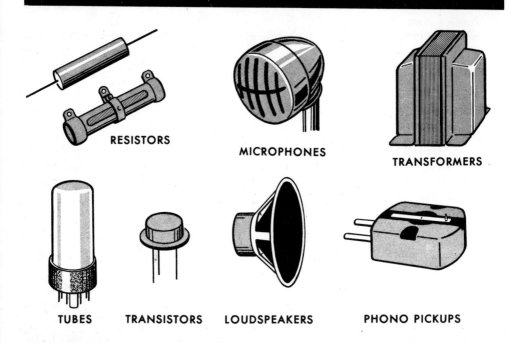

Components with Resistance

RESISTORS

MICROPHONES

TRANSFORMERS

TUBES TRANSISTORS LOUDSPEAKERS PHONO PICKUPS

are Sources of Noise Energy

As most audio equipment is operated at room temperature and the noise voltages cannot be measured very precisely anyway, we need only deal with an average figure. The energy output depends on the overall range of frequencies involved. If we use measurements that include frequencies from 0 to 20,000 cycles, the energy will be twice that for frequencies from 0 to 10,000 cycles.

Noise and Bandwidth

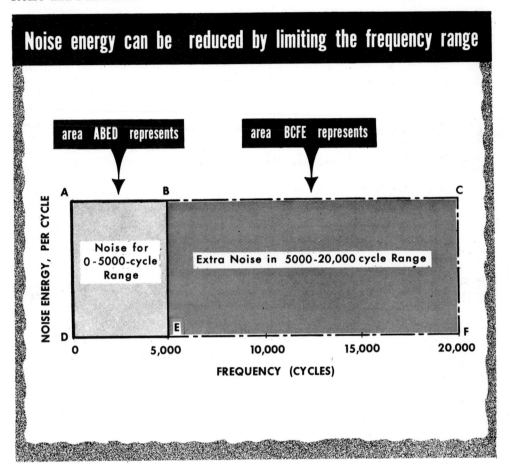

Noise energy can be reduced by limiting the frequency range

area **ABED** represents

area **BCFE** represents

Noise for 0-5000-cycle Range

Extra Noise in 5000-20,000 cycle Range

NOISE ENERGY, PER CYCLE

FREQUENCY (CYCLES)

At an average room temperature, the noise energy of any resistor is .0165 micromicromicrowatt, or .000 000 000 000 000 000 0165 watt, per cycle. If we take the bandwidth as 10,000 cycles, the noise energy will be 165 micromicromicrowatts. Once we know the value of the resistance, we can calculate the noise *voltage* it will produce, by the usual formula, $E = \sqrt{P \times R}$. For example, for a 1-megohm resistor (1,000,000 ohms), the noise voltage for a bandwidth of 10,000 cycles is:

$$\sqrt{.0165\ \mu\mu\mu\ \text{watt} \times 10,000 \times 1,000,000\ \text{ohms}} = \sqrt{165\ \mu\mu\ \text{volts}} = 12.9\ \mu\ \text{volts}.$$

This suggests one convenient way to reduce effective noise when that is a severe problem. By reducing the frequency range at the high end, say from 20,000 cycles to 5,000 cycles, we lose 2 octaves of audio (and the top one doesn't have much in it anyway) and we reduce the noise in the ratio of 4 to 1, or 6 db. This technique is useful for communications work.

Noise in Tubes and Transistors

Both tubes and transistors generate noise components. For a tube this can be measured and calculated as an effective resistance value connected between grid and cathode. Changing the amplified bandwidth will modify the noise voltage in exactly the same way as it does with an ordinary resistor. The value of resistance calculated from measurements shown serves to give the effective noise the tube will produce, however the circuit happens to be arranged.

In transistors, the calculations for noise source are not as simple as in tubes. Connection between emitter and base and between collector and base each are associated with a resistance value inside the transistor. Each of these effective resistances causes a noise component, in the way just discussed, although neither of them is a constant resistance value. The input and output resistance are dependent on each other and dependent on the temperature of the transistor at its critical junction point. This temperature, in turn, is dependent on the combined currents, which produce a small amount of heat. These fluctuations also cause noise, which is predominant at low frequencies.

MEASURING A TUBE'S EQUIVALENT NOISE RESISTANCE

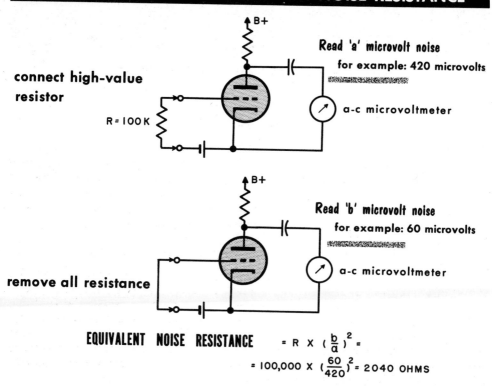

connect high-value resistor

R = 100 K

Read 'a' microvolt noise
for example: 420 microvolts

a-c microvoltmeter

remove all resistance

Read 'b' microvolt noise
for example: 60 microvolts

a-c microvoltmeter

EQUIVALENT NOISE RESISTANCE $= R \times (\frac{b}{a})^2 =$

$= 100{,}000 \times (\frac{60}{420})^2 = 2040$ OHMS

The Effect of a Step-Up Transformer

The Audio Transformer steps up the *Noise Voltage* as well as the *Audio Voltage*

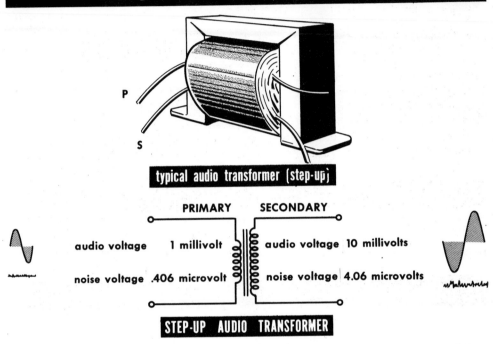

typical audio transformer (step-up)

STEP-UP AUDIO TRANSFORMER

When a transformer is used to step up the audio voltages from a microphone or pickup, it steps up the noise voltage that comes with it. Suppose the audio voltage is 1 millivolt, and the resistance of the microphone or pickup is 500 ohms. In a bandwidth of 20,000 cycles (which we expect for high fidelity), the noise voltage from 500 ohms is

$$\sqrt{.0165 \text{ micromicromicrowatt} \times 20,000 \times 500 \text{ ohms}}$$
$$= \sqrt{.165 \times \text{micromicrovolts}} = 0.406 \text{ microvolt}$$

If we use a step-up transformer to raise the 1 millivolt to 10 millivolts, the voltage is stepped up 10 times, the current down by 10:1, and total power transferred remains the same. This means the effective resistance (voltage divided by current) is multiplied 100 times. The 0.406-microvolt noise signal will be stepped up with the 1 millivolt audio to become 4.06 microvolts of noise. In this statement, we have not considered any possible noise the transformer may add of its own, due to the resistance of its windings and core magnetization effects.

Input Transformers

An input transformer is used to improve the signal-to-noise ratio in certain circumstances. If the noise resistance of a tube is 2000 ohms and the impedance or resistance of a microphone is only 500 ohms, the predominant noise when the microphone is connected in directly will be due to the tube. In fact, the tube will produce twice the noise voltage, for a given bandwidth, that the microphone does.

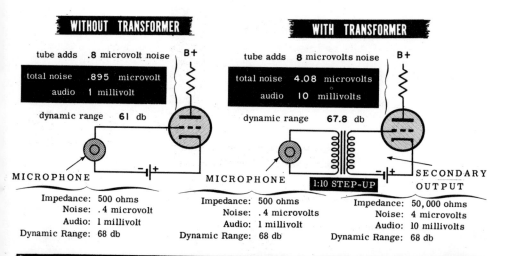

Input Transformer improves signal-to-noise ratio

With the microphone producing 0.4 microvolt of noise, and the tube 0.8 microvolt of noise, the two add together by the process of "the square root of the squares"; 0.4 squared is 0.16 and 0.8 squared is 0.64. Adding these figures gives 0.8, the square root of which is 0.895 microvolt with an audio voltage of, say, 1 millivolt.

By stepping up the audio and microphone noise with a 10:1 input transformer, the microphone gives 4 microvolts of noise on the transformer secondary. The tube still gives 0.8 microvolt of noise. Now the total noise voltage is $\sqrt{4^2 + .8^2} = \sqrt{16 + .64} = 4.08$ microvolts, which is very little more than the microphone alone. The audio voltage, however, has been stepped up to 10 millivolts in place of the original 1 millivolt. Thus signal-to-noise ratio has been improved by better than 2:1. Beyond this point, however, using a transformer with greater step-up will not improve matters, because it will step up the audio and the noise in the same ratio. In addition, making a transformer with a big step-up gives problems in getting uniform response over a wide range of frequencies.

Nonlinear Amplification

Grid voltage/plate current *curves* are always that—curved. Because of this curvature, the same change in input voltage will not always cause the same change in output current and voltage. For example, a negative change of 1 volt may produce a 2-milliampere change in plate current, accompanied by a 40-volt change in plate potential (using a plate load resistor of 20,000 ohms); a positive change of 1 volt may produce a 2.5-milliampere change in plate current, accompanied by a 50-volt change in plate potential.

The positive half of a wave will thus get amplified more than the negative half. At the input both positive and negative halves of the wave measure 1 volt, but at the output the negative half is 50 volts, and the positive half is 40 volts. This distortion of the wave is due to the curvature or nonlinearity of the tube characteristic.

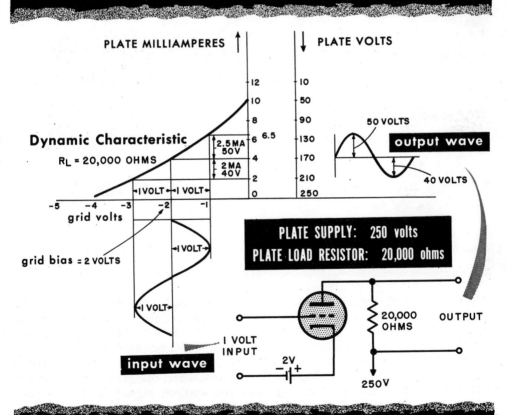

Nonlinear amplification causes distorted output

PLATE MILLIAMPERES ↑   ↓ PLATE VOLTS

Dynamic Characteristic
R_L = 20,000 OHMS

2.5 MA
50V

2 MA
40V

←I VOLT→←I VOLT→

-5   -4   -3   -2   -1
grid volts

grid bias = 2 VOLTS

←I VOLT→

←I VOLT→

I VOLT
INPUT

input wave

output wave

50 VOLTS

40 VOLTS

PLATE SUPPLY: 250 volts
PLATE LOAD RESISTOR: 20,000 ohms

20,000
OHMS

OUTPUT

2V
− +

250V

DISTORTION EFFECTS

Clipping

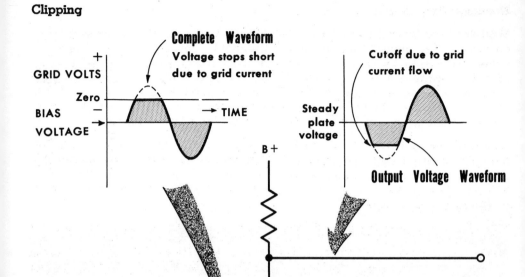

GRID CLIPPING results when the grid voltage passes the zero point and current begins to flow in the grid circuit

Another kind of distortion occurs because the input fluctuations abruptly cease to produce a corresponding output fluctuation. The most common cause of this is known as *grid clipping*. Normal amplification takes advantage of the fact that, when the grid has a negative voltage, no grid current flows. When the grid passes the zero point between negative and positive, however, grid current *will* start to flow. Thus, when the grid is negative, no current flows in the grid circuit, and the applied signal is undistorted. When the grid reaches the zero point, however, it starts to draw current, and "short-circuits" positive-going voltage beyond that point.

USE OF THE OSCILLOSCOPE

Showing Waveforms with the Oscilloscope

Waveforms can actually be examined by means of the instrument known as an oscilloscope. It uses a special tube in which a beam or "pencil" of electrons is focused to a point on a fluorescent screen that glows with the impact of the electrons. Two pairs of deflecting plates bend the beam in accordance with the voltages applied to them.

Applying different voltages to the plates at the sides of the beam will move the spot sideways, and voltages applied to the upper and lower plates deflect the beam up or down. If different fluctuating voltages are applied to both pairs of plates, the spot will trace a pattern on the screen representing the combined effect of the two voltage fluctuations.

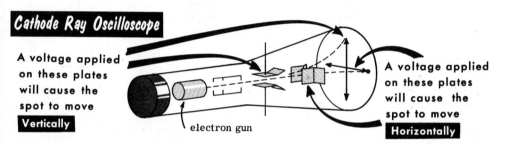

Cathode Ray Oscilloscope

A voltage applied on these plates will cause the spot to move **Vertically**

electron gun

A voltage applied on these plates will cause the spot to move **Horizontally**

If the fluctuation applied to the side plates follows a "sawtooth" waveform, the spot will move steadily from left to right across the screen, and then rapidly return to its starting point. By using this waveform as a "time-base" in this way, the voltage applied to the vertical plates traces its own waveform. In this way we can see the curvature distortion or clipping just discussed.

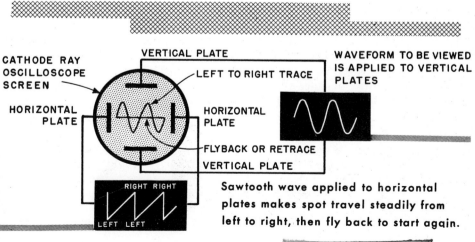

CATHODE RAY OSCILLOSCOPE SCREEN

VERTICAL PLATE

LEFT TO RIGHT TRACE

HORIZONTAL PLATE

HORIZONTAL PLATE

FLYBACK OR RETRACE

VERTICAL PLATE

RIGHT RIGHT

LEFT LEFT

WAVEFORM TO BE VIEWED IS APPLIED TO VERTICAL PLATES

Sawtooth wave applied to horizontal plates makes spot travel steadily from left to right, then fly back to start again.

(2-57)

Showing Simple Patterns with the Oscilloscope

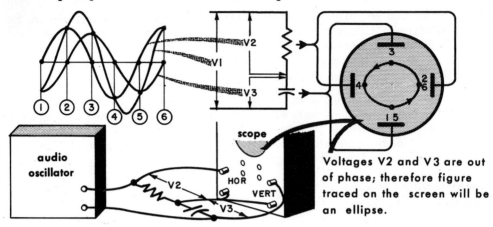

Voltages V2 and V3 are out
of phase; therefore figure
traced on the screen will be
an ellipse.

When a resistor and capacitor are connected in series, the same current must flow through both. The voltage across the resistor is always proportional to the current through it. The voltage across the capacitor, however, depends on the instantaneous charge on it, which is constantly changed by the fluctuating current. Of course the current does not flow *through* the capacitor, although that expression is often used. What really happens is that current reaching the capacitor changes the charge on it and, with it, the voltage across the capacitor. This voltage changes in proportion to the instantaneous current reaching it. A bigger current will change the voltage more rapidly.

When a sinusoidal voltage fluctuation is applied to the resistor-capacitor combination, there will be two sine waves, one across the resistor and one across the capacitor. The waves will have a time difference, such that the steepest slope on one coincides with the peak on the other. By applying the voltage from the resistor to one pair of oscilloscope plates, and that across the capacitor to the others, the spot will be made to travel up and down and from side to side, but because the two movements are not synchronized, the spot traces an ellipse. If both pairs of plates are connected across resistors, so the voltages always vary in proportion, the spot will travel along a sloping line, because the up-and-down and the sideways movements always occur at the same time and in proportion.

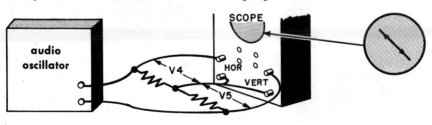

Showing the Effect of Frequency

Because the *fluctuation* of charge on a capacitor is something that takes time, the division of audio voltage drops between a capacitor and resistor in series will differ according to the applied frequency.

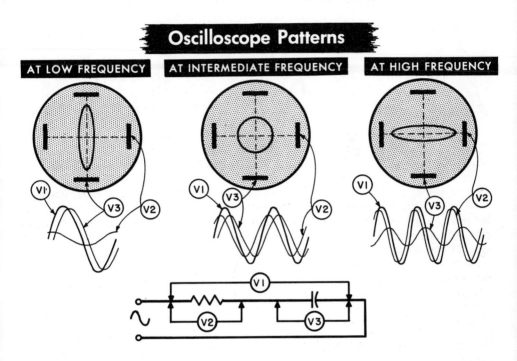

Oscilloscope Patterns

| AT LOW FREQUENCY | AT INTERMEDIATE FREQUENCY | AT HIGH FREQUENCY |

At a high frequency, a charge on the capacitor does not have time to change very much, and most of the voltage fluctuation appears across the resistor. At a low frequency, the charge on the capacitor has plenty of time to change, and can do so with a comparatively small current flowing through the resistor. Consequently, most of the voltage fluctuation appears across the capacitor. At an intermediate frequency the two voltages are about equal. Both of them are sine waves and they are "spaced" apart in time by a phase difference of 90°.

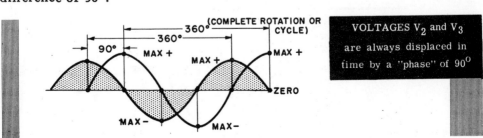

VOLTAGES V_2 and V_3 are always displaced in time by a "phase" of 90°

Arrangements of R and C

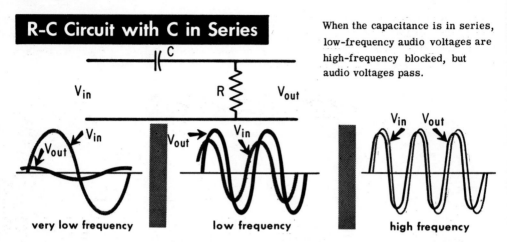

R-C Circuit with C in Series

When the capacitance is in series, low-frequency audio voltages are high-frequency blocked, but audio voltages pass.

V_{in} C   R V_{out}

V_{out} V_{in} **very low frequency**

V_{out} V_{in} **low frequency**

V_{in} V_{out} **high frequency**

The effect of this frequency discrimination of resistance and capacitance in the same circuit depends on the way the components are used. If the capacitance is in series with the audio signal, it will tend to stop the low frequencies, blocking d-c altogether and losing most of the voltages at the extremely low frequencies. At high frequencies, all of the audio voltage will be transferred through the capacitor. The coupling capacitor between stages of amplification used is in this position of capacitance, which means that it produces a loss of low-frequency response.

On the other hand, if the capacitance is in shunt, or so that the audio signal at the output of the arrangement appears across the capacitance, then its presence will mean that high frequencies almost disappear.

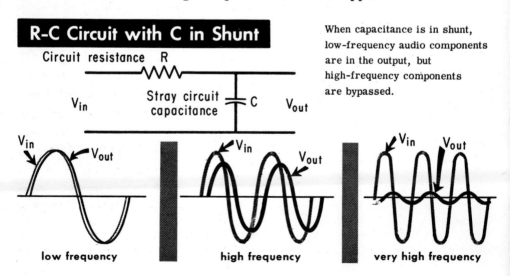

R-C Circuit with C in Shunt

When capacitance is in shunt, low-frequency audio components are in the output, but high-frequency components are bypassed.

Circuit resistance   R

V_{in} Stray circuit capacitance   C V_{out}

V_{in} V_{out} **low frequency**

V_{in} V_{out} **high frequency**

V_{in} V_{out} **very high frequency**

Capacitive Reactance

The ratio between the voltage across and the current through a capacitor at a specified frequency is called its *reactance*. This is valued in *ohms* like a resistance. But where voltage and current in a resistance are simultaneous, there is a time (or *phase)* difference (of 90°) in a reactance.

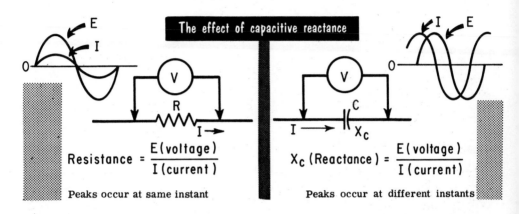

The effect of capacitive reactance

$$\text{Resistance} = \frac{E(\text{voltage})}{I(\text{current})}$$

Peaks occur at same instant

$$X_c(\text{Reactance}) = \frac{E(\text{voltage})}{I(\text{current})}$$

Peaks occur at different instants

When the reactance of a capacitor is equal to the circuit resistance, the voltage across it is equal to that across the circuit resistance. At this frequency the phase between the input and output will be 45°, and the voltage output will be 0.707 of the voltage input or 3 db down.

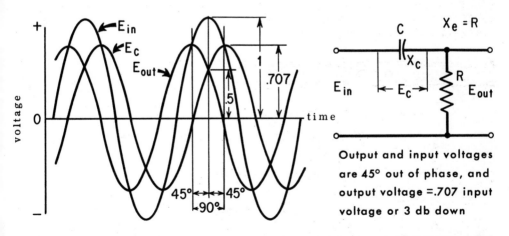

Output and input voltages are 45° out of phase, and output voltage =.707 input voltage or 3 db down

Notice that making the two voltages (E_c and E_{out}) equal does not mean that either of them is equal to *half* the input voltage (E_{in}), because there is a 90° phase angle between the voltage across the capacitance and that across the resistance. For this reason, the two voltage drops cannot be added arithmetically.

Distributed Capacitance

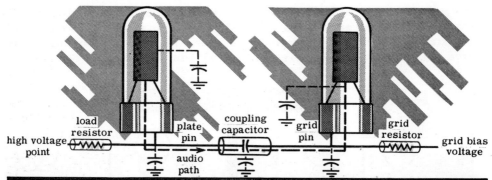

Stray capacitance that loses high frequencies is distributed everywhere in the audio circuit

Loss of high-frequency response occurs because of capacitance we cannot avoid, although it is not in the form of an actual capacitor. A capacitor is a component in which natural capacitance is exaggerated by putting large areas of foil in close proximity to one another. This produces capacitance values that are measured in microfarads. However, the presence of electrical circuits (conductors, components, chassis) in the same space produces a capacitance between different points, although it is measured only in micromicrofarads.

It is this capacitance that causes loss of high frequencies. At the frequency where the reactance of the total capacitance between the audio circuit and ground is equal to the effective circuit resistance, there will be a phase shift of 45° and 3-db loss in audio level.

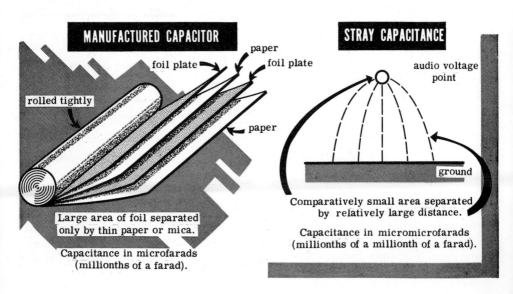

Improving Low-Frequency Response

Now that we know the action of the basic components, we can see what will happen by changing their values. First, consider the effect of changing the plate coupling resistor. In the case of a triode tube, the plate resistance of the tube is between plate and ground, while the plate coupling resistor is between plate and B+. The B+ supply will invariably have a very large capacitor coupling the high voltage to ground, so it is impossible for the B+ voltage to vary relative to ground. Any audio currents that reach the B+ point will be bypassed to ground through the large output capacitance in the B+ supply.

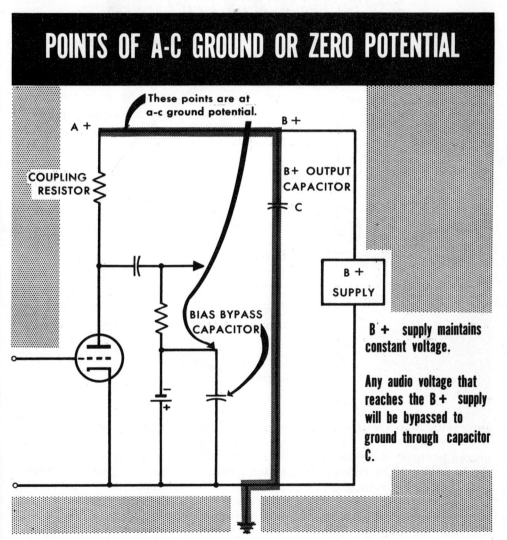

POINTS OF A-C GROUND OR ZERO POTENTIAL

These points are at a-c ground potential.

A+

B+

COUPLING RESISTOR

B+ OUTPUT CAPACITOR

C

BIAS BYPASS CAPACITOR

B+ SUPPLY

B+ supply maintains constant voltage.

Any audio voltage that reaches the B+ supply will be bypassed to ground through capacitor C.

Improving Low-Frequency Response (contd.)

In the case of a triode tube, the coupling resistor is usually larger than the plate resistance of the tube because the a-c resistance of a triode is much lower than its d-c resistance. The plate coupling resistor will be about equal to the d-c resistance of the tube, so that about half the B+ voltage drops across the coupling resistor and half across the tube.

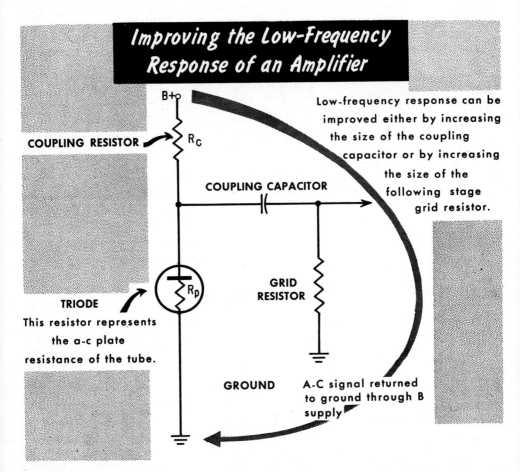

Improving the Low-Frequency Response of an Amplifier

Low-frequency response can be improved either by increasing the size of the coupling capacitor or by increasing the size of the following stage grid resistor.

COUPLING RESISTOR   R_C

B+

COUPLING CAPACITOR

TRIODE
This resistor represents the a-c plate resistance of the tube.

R_p

GRID RESISTOR

GROUND

A-C signal returned to ground through B supply

Improving the low-frequency response requires the use of either a larger coupling capacitor or larger resistances in the associated circuit. When the preceding tube is a triode, increasing the coupling resistor will not effectively increase the resistance for audio voltages from the plate to ground because this resistance is limited by the plate resistance of the tube. The only possibility of considerably increasing the resistance associated with the coupling capacitor is to increase the following stage grid resistor. Alternatively, the coupling capacitor can be increased in value.

Improving High-Frequency Response (contd.)

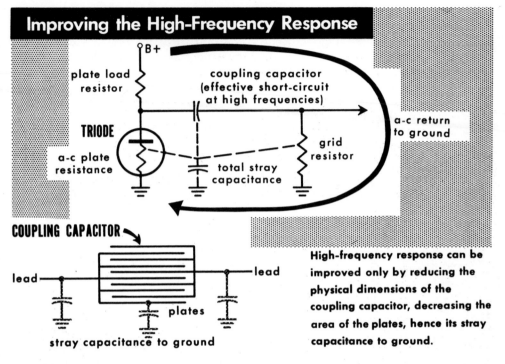

Improving the High-Frequency Response

High-frequency response can be improved only by reducing the physical dimensions of the coupling capacitor, decreasing the area of the plates, hence its stray capacitance to ground.

For high-frequency signals, the coupling capacitor is effectively a short circuit—no audio voltages appear across it, and both sides of the capacitor are at the same audio voltage at any instant. This means that we now have three effective resistance paths to ground from the plate of the tube: through the plate resistance of the tube, through the coupling resistor, and through the following stage's grid resistor.

Improving high-frequency response can be achieved by reducing the small capacitances to ground or reducing the total circuit resistance to ground. In the case of a triode amplifier, the lowest individual resistance (which principally controls the effective parallel resistance of the combination) is the plate resistance of the tube, which is fixed by the tube type. Consequently the best way to approach getting better high-frequency response is to see how we can reduce the capacitance.

One way to reduce capacitance is to use a smaller coupling capacitor (smaller in actual dimensions, rather than smaller in value). The coupling capacitor, like all other parts of the audio wiring, will add to the capacitance to ground, in addition to providing the requisite capacitance between its plates. The only way to reduce its capacitance to ground is to use a capacitor of smaller dimensions, so that it does not have such a large surface to provide capacitance to ground.

Improving the Frequency Response of a Pentode Stage

Using a pentode tube for the stage before the coupling alters the situation. Here the plate resistance is usually much larger than the load resistance, because the a-c resistance of a pentode is much greater than its d-c resistance. This means that the load resistance used with a pentode exercises the principal control on the plate-to-ground resistance. Using a larger coupling resistor, as well as increasing gain (which it naturally does with a pentode), will improve the low-frequency response, because it increases the resistance in series with the coupling capacitor. At the same time, the increased load resistance will reduce the high-frequency response because it makes the total resistance to ground higher.

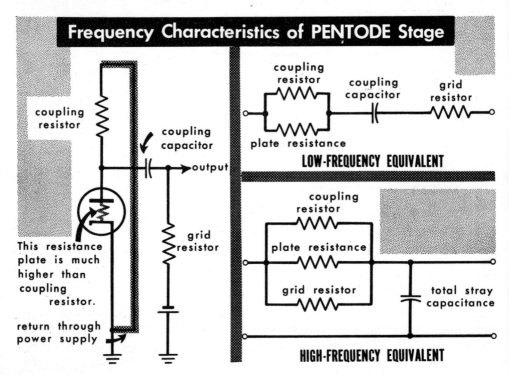

Thus whichever type of tube we use, there are optimum (or best) combinations of circuit values to get the kind of response we want: a response that is good enough, but not unnecessarily good. In each case, struggling too hard to get a good low-frequency response will give us problems at the high-frequency end, and vice versa. Further than this, if we struggle to get a good frequency response at both ends we shall get less gain from the amplifier. The values that we use will be such that the first tube cannot develop as much gain as it would if we were content with a frequency response that was not quite so uniform.

Power-Limiting Factors

The discussion thus far has been about getting audio *voltage* from tubes. To be able to hear sound from the loudspeaker, however, we need *power*. The loudspeaker needs *watts* to drive it, not just *volts*. For every watt audio of output that we get, there must be some power dissipated in the output tube, because the audio current in the plate circuit of the tube that goes to the voice-coil circuit also has to go through the tube.

This means that some power must be used up in the tube, which, in turn, makes the tube get hot. Thus there is a power limit on the tube before it will start to destroy itself. This limit is determined by the size of the internal components of the tube and the arrangements made by the tube designer to dissipate the heat. The manufacturer always specifies the maximum power dissipation of a tube intended for power-output use.

The tube is always in series with the load or impedance into which the power is fed because the tube is basically a *current* controlling device. This means the same current fluctuations flow in the tube as in the output circuit. By using a higher supply voltage, it is possible to drop a smaller *proportion* of the output power in the tube and get a larger proportion into the output circuit. It is thus advantageous to use a higher supply voltage because it gives better efficiency. This unfortunately brings us against another limitation. For any particular tube, there is a limit to the working voltage that may be used before some kind of breakdown might occur. This limit also is usually specified by the tube manufacturer.

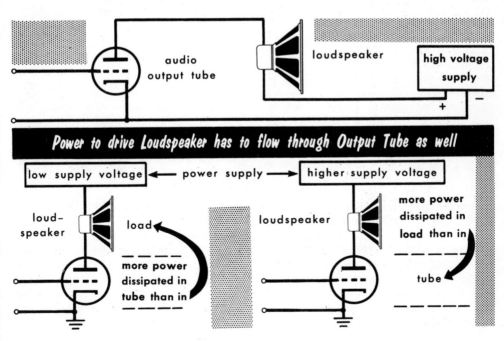

Improving Power Output

Let us start with the simplest tube circuit and see the various steps that are taken toward improving the available power output. Suppose we use a large version of the ordinary triode tube used for voltage amplification that will handle more power, using a plate coupling resistor and capacitor to get the power into the load.

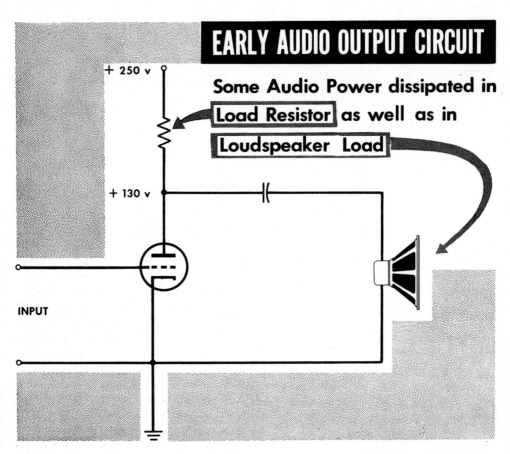

We shall also have to use a high-impedance load suitable to the tube. (This was the way some early radio sets were designed.) Suppose that B+ is 250 volts and that we drop 120 volts in the load resistor. This means the plate potential will be 130 volts. (It will fluctuate, due to the audio, above and below 130 volts, and this fluctuation will be passed through the coupling capacitor to the load.) The audio fluctuation also appears across the plate coupling resistor, hence it will get not only the power necessary to feed the tube with plate current, but also some of the audio power due to the current fluctuations flowing through it.

Transformer Coupling

The first step toward improving the efficiency of a power-output stage is to eliminate this loss in the plate coupling resistor by using choke coupling. (This avoids the d-c drop in the plate load component.) We still get the audio fluctuations across the choke due to its *inductance,* but the fluctuations are too rapid to allow the current in the choke to fluctuate. The current fluctuations produced by the tube are all delivered through the coupling capacitor to the load. In this way we can use a B+ supply of 130 volts and still get the same total audio power from the tube as before, using a 250-volt supply.

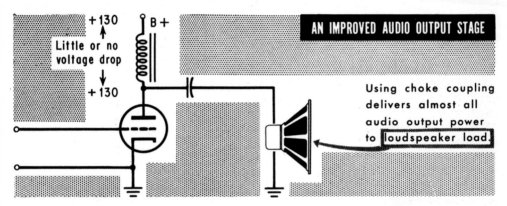

+130 B+

Little or no
voltage drop

+ 130

AN IMPROVED AUDIO OUTPUT STAGE

Using choke coupling delivers almost all audio output power to loudspeaker load.

We can save a component here by eliminating the coupling capacitor. We do this by putting two windings on the choke, converting it into a transformer. The winding connected between the plate of the tube and B+ has a large number of turns, whereas the other winding has a much smaller number of turns. This means the audio current fluctuations are stepped up, while the voltage fluctuations are stepped down to suit a lower impedance load; the tube, however, operates as if it had the requisite high-value load resistance connected between the plate and B+.

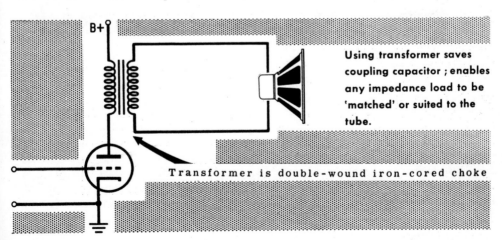

B+

Using transformer saves coupling capacitor ; enables any impedance load to be 'matched' or suited to the tube.

Transformer is double-wound iron-cored choke

POWER AMPLIFICATION

Transformer Coupling (contd.)

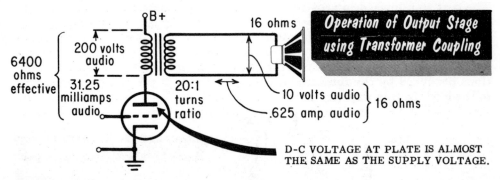

Operation of Output Stage using Transformer Coupling

D-C VOLTAGE AT PLATE IS ALMOST THE SAME AS THE SUPPLY VOLTAGE.

Suppose that the load resistance connected to the secondary is 16 ohms and the transformer step down ratio is 20:1. This means the voltage fluctuations will be stepped down by 20:1 and the corresponding current fluctuation stepped *up* by 20:1. The impedance will be transformed by a ratio of 400:1, producing an effective resistance at the primary of (400 $\times$ 16) or 6400 ohms. This is called the load resistance referred to the primary or referred resistance for short. The d-c voltage drop between B+ and the plate will be quite small—only about 10 volts.

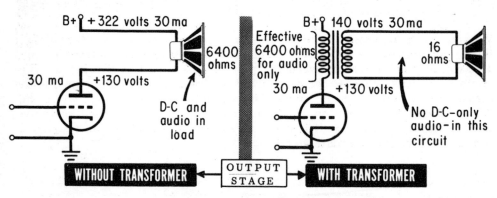

Suppose that the operating point chosen for the tube is 30 milliamperes at 130 volts. A current of 30 milliamperes through 6400 ohms produces 192 volts. The transformer-coupled circuit thus works as if the B+ supply were 130 + 192 or 322 volts, with a 6400-ohm resistor connected between plate and B+ for a load. However, the 30 millamperes are not flowing through the load resistor actually in the circuit (16 ohms), but only through the primary resistance of the transformer, which may produce a drop of about 10 volts and thus require a supply of only 140 volts at 30 milliamperes to get 130 volts at the plate, instead of 322 volts at 30 milliamperes. Furthermore, all of the power developed by the tube is matched to the load, which can be any desired impedance, if the transformer ratio is correctly chosen.

The Effect of Changing the Load

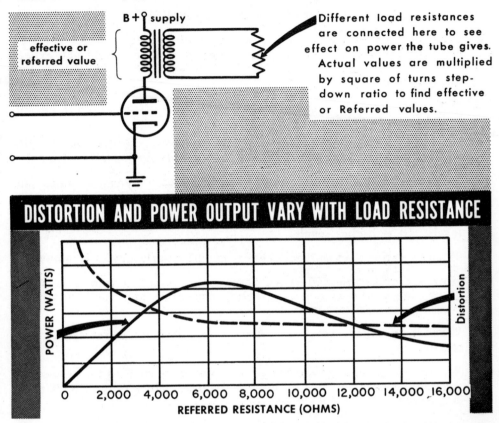

effective or referred value

B + supply

Different load resistances are connected here to see effect on power the tube gives. Actual values are multiplied by square of turns step-down ratio to find effective or Referred values.

DISTORTION AND POWER OUTPUT VARY WITH LOAD RESISTANCE

POWER (WATTS) — Distortion

REFERRED RESISTANCE (OHMS): 0 2,000 4,000 6,000 8,000 10,000 12,000 14,000 16,000

With choke or transformer coupling, we can try the effect of applying different load values to the same tube. If we use referred resistance values slightly higher than the plate resistance of the tube, the waveform of the output follows the input waveform quite closely and there is little distortion. Continuing the increase in load resistance, however, the voltage fluctuation fairly quickly reaches a maximum and doubling the resistance value does not result in a proportionate increase in the voltage developed. For this reason, the power obtained drops off almost in inverse proportion to the increase in load value.

Making the referred load resistance the same as the plate resistance of the tube gives about the maximum power output obtainable, but causes considerable distortion in the output, due to the curvature of tube characteristics. If a high-quality power output is required, the load resistance must be at least two or three times as great as the plate resistance of the tube. Taking the load resistance value even lower than the plate resistance of the tube results in increased distortion and reduced power output.

QUESTIONS AND PROBLEMS

1. What limits the dynamic range that an amplifier can handle?

2. What is the difference between the dynamic range of a single stage of amplification and that of a complete amplifier? How would you expect dynamic range to vary with (a) the total amplifier gain, (b) its frequency response?

3. Why does most noise in audio systems manifest itself as a hissing sound from the loudspeaker?

4. Why does a communications receiver use a very limited bandwidth, while a high-fidelity system should have a wide frequency response?

5. How can an input transformer help to increase dynamic range, and under what conditions will it do so?

6. What is the predominant cause of distortion in amplifiers (a) at low levels, (b) at higher levels?

7. What is a time base, and for what is it particularly useful in audio?

8. How does the time difference between input and output sine waves occur, due to the effects of coupling capacitors and how can this be shown on an oscilloscope?

9. What is capacitive reactance? How does reactance differ from resistance?

10. When the reactance in a circuit rises to a point equal to the resistance, the voltage does not drop to half its original value. Why? Explain the significance of the *3-db point*.

11. Explain how circuit resistance values in the coupling between amplifying stages can affect frequency response, and show what are the important quantities for low- and high-frequency response, both for triode and pentode stages.

12. What is the essential difference between the uses of tubes for voltage amplification and for power amplification?

13. Why is resistance-capacitance coupling, so often used for voltage amplifiers, not economic for power stages?

14. Explain the advantages of a transformer for power-stage couping.

15. How does a pentode improve the possibilities of performance (a) of a voltage amplifier, (b) of a power-output stage?

16. What is the difference between a pentode and a beam power tube? Can either of these tubes be connected in such a way as to work as a triode?

Push-Pull

The next step in improving the power output capacity of an amplifier stage is to use two tubes in a connection known as *push-pull*. This arrangement uses transformer coupling, but there are two primaries (the primary winding has two halves), through which the current flows in opposite directions. B+ is connected to the center point of the primary, with the plate of one of the tubes connected to each end. The current, therefore, flows from each plate outward through an equal number of turns to the center point. This means that the total magnetizing effect on the core of the transformer is neutralized as far as the d-c is concerned. (The transformer core only has to carry the magnetization due to the audio fluctuation.) This simplifies the design and cost of the transformer, but the big advantage is in tube operation.

With a single tube, matching the output load to the tube plate resistance results in a poor output waveform, which takes the form of a rounding at the bottom and sharpening at the top. When the tubes are worked in push-pull, the current flows in opposite directions around the transformer core and, consequently, what is the top of the current waveform in the upper part of the winding becomes the bottom of the current waveform in the lower half of the winding. Thus both halves of the current waveform have a sharpened portion added to a rounded portion, and the effect averages out, producing a much better waveform for the load value used. To achieve this, we must provide the correct audio voltages at the grids of the tubes. We shall consider this problem presently.

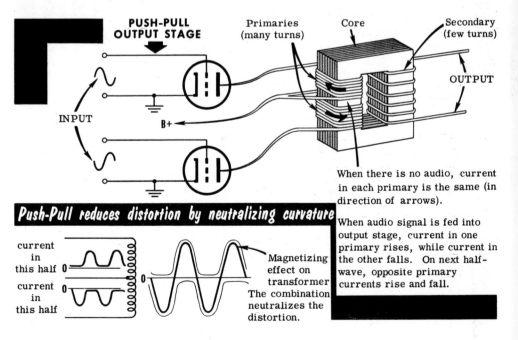

PUSH-PULL OUTPUT STAGE — Primaries (many turns) — Core — Secondary (few turns) — OUTPUT — INPUT — B+

When there is no audio, current in each primary is the same (in direction of arrows).

Push-Pull reduces distortion by neutralizing curvature

current in this half — current in this half

Magnetizing effect on transformer. The combination neutralizes the distortion.

When audio signal is fed into output stage, current in one primary rises, while current in the other falls. On next half-wave, opposite primary currents rise and fall.

The Development of The Pentode

The next circuit improvement comes from the design of the tube itself. We already mentioned the use of a pentode for voltage amplification. Tube development, however, was originally carried out to improve power output. The effect of plate voltage swing in reducing plate current swing in a triode tube, cuts down its power-handling capacity by an even greater amount than it does its voltage-handling capacity.

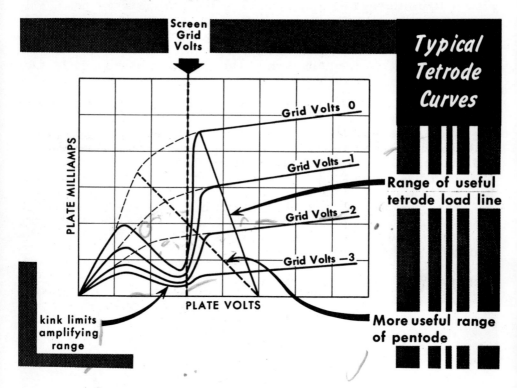

The first development from the triode was the tetrode, made by inserting only the second (screen) grid. This was found to result in an improvement in power output, although it was limited by secondary emission. When the plate potential is lower than that on the screen grid, electrons bounced off by the impact of arriving electrons at the plate will be attracted to the screen, resulting in plate current curves that give a curious kink and limit the range over which the tube can be successfully used for normal amplifying purposes.

The pentode overcomes this difficulty by using the third (suppressor) grid which prevents any electrons bounced off the plate from traveling back to the screen or second grid under any circumstances. All such electrons are repelled by the suppressor grid and sent back to the plate.

The Beam-Power Tetrode

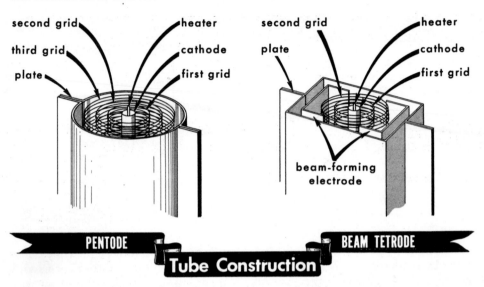

second grid   heater
third grid   cathode
plate   first grid

second grid   heater
plate   cathode
    first grid

beam-forming electrode

PENTODE   **BEAM TETRODE**

Tube Construction

Another method of preventing secondary emission uses a specially shaped electrode between the screen grid and the plate. It is called a *beam-forming* electrode and consists of two pieces of metal placed in a different direction from the grid wires of the normal grid. (The normal grid wires are wound around the cathode at a constant radius; beam-forming electrodes run parallel to the cathode in specially selected positions.) It is connected to the cathode in just the same way as the suppressor grid of the pentode, and its effect on performance is very similar to that given by the addition of a suppressor grid. It succeeds in squeezing the last ounce of efficiency out of the tube, by extending the voltage and current swing to the maximum possible degree.

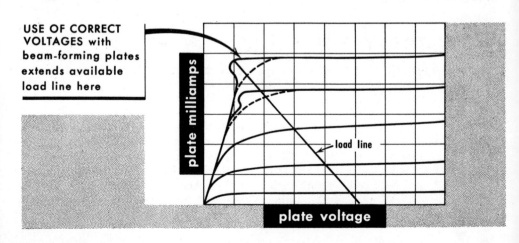

USE OF CORRECT VOLTAGES with beam-forming plates extends available load line here

plate milliamps

load line

plate voltage

Triode Connection of Pentodes

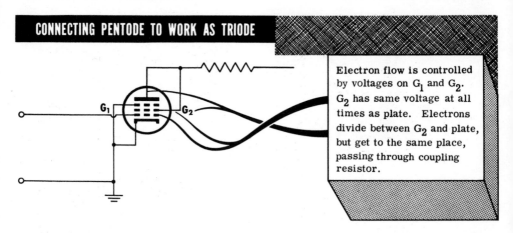

CONNECTING PENTODE TO WORK AS TRIODE

G_1 G_2

Electron flow is controlled by voltages on G_1 and G_2. G_2 has same voltage at all times as plate. Electrons divide between G_2 and plate, but get to the same place, passing through coupling resistor.

Any pentode-type tube can be made to work as a triode-type tube. This is done by connecting the second grid directly to the plate, so that both swing together at the same voltage. Because the screen grid, in combination with the control grid, is principally responsible for controlling the plate current, the presence of the suppressor grid between the screen grid and plate does not materially alter the tube's performance from that of a triode.

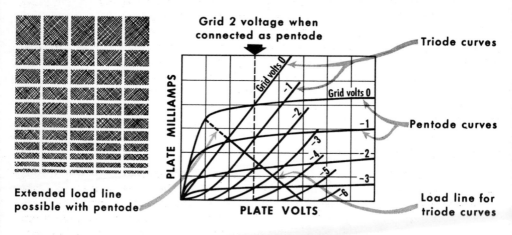

Grid 2 voltage when connected as pentode

Triode curves

Grid volts 0

Pentode curves

PLATE MILLIAMPS

Grid volts 0
−1
−2
−3
−4
−5
−6
−1
−2
−3

PLATE VOLTS

Extended load line possible with pentode

Load line for triode curves

Using the best possible load resistance with triode-connected tubes, the voltage fluctuation between B+ and plate reaches little more than half the B+ supply voltage. Changing the method of connection to pentode alters the curve so that the zero grid-voltage curve is pushed out into a "knee." This extends, very considerably, both the voltage and current fluctuation available in the plate circuit. This, in turn, triples or quadruples the power that any pair of tubes will give.

The Lowering of Distortion

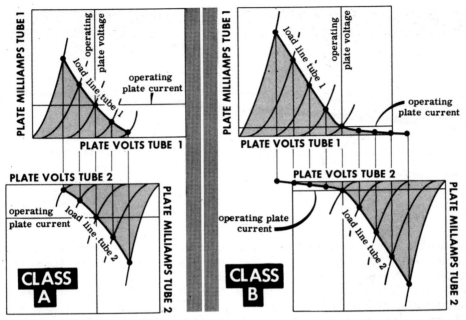

Using two tubes in push-pull helps the waveform problems, so that the distortion produced by one tube cancels that produced by the other. This can be understood better if we think of each tube as having a *curved* load line. The input voltages to the grids are equal but 180° out of phase. The plate voltages likewise are out of phase because of the coupling between the two primary windings of the output transformer. So the changes in plate current must adjust between the tubes to allow this condition, while the two of them supply the *total* current fluctuation to the load at all points. The ratio between total voltage and current fluctuation of both tubes is set by the load resistance matched to the secondary of the transformer, but each tube feeds a load resistance whose value is constantly changing, as represented by the curves.

This effect can be extended further to increase the efficiency of the output stage. Normally the steady plate current is about half the maximum plate current (which occurs when the grid voltage fluctuation goes from the operating point up to zero). The current fluctuation in the tube at maximum power level swings between almost zero current and twice the steady current. This sets a considerable limitation on the power-handling capacity of the tube because the steady component is such a large proportion of the maximum current the tubes take. Using a greater negative bias on the grids of the tubes makes the audio fluctuations carry the current from almost zero up to a maximum in one direction and cuts the tube off so that no current flows in the other direction. This makes possible a considerable increase in efficiency and available power output.

Power Output from a Class-A Stage

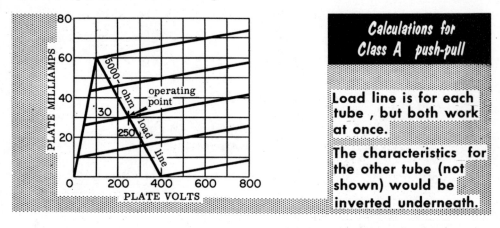

Calculations for Class A push-pull

Load line is for each tube, but both work at once.

The characteristics for the other tube (not shown) would be inverted underneath.

As an example, suppose that in ordinary push-pull (known as *class A,* which means that both tubes are conducting current all the time), the operating point for each tube is 250 volts at 30 milliamperes and that the load value presented to each tube is 5000 ohms with pentode operation. Disregarding the curves to make the calculation simpler (if approximate), the audio fluctuation should carry the plate between 100 volts at 60 milliamperes and 400 volts at zero milliamperes. This represents a peak fluctuation from each tube of 150 volts and 30 milliamps in each direction, which is a peak power of (150 $\times$ .03) or 4.5 watts per tube or 9 watts for the two tubes in push-pull. The average power, using a sine wave to drive the output, will be just half of this figure or 4.5 watts for the two tubes.

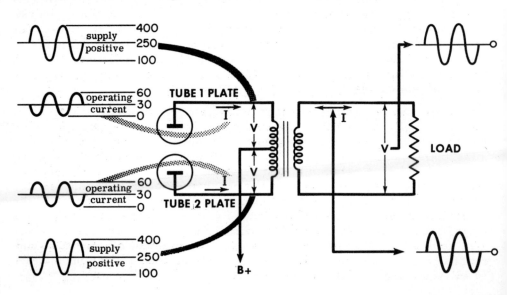

Class-B Operation

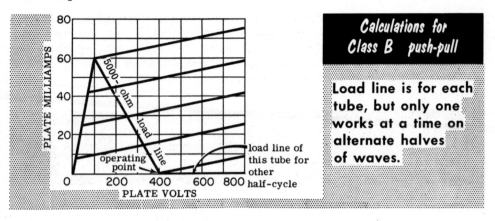

Calculations for Class B push-pull

Load line is for each tube, but only one works at a time on alternate halves of waves.

If we wish to use an extreme economy measure, known as *class-B* operation, we bias each tube back approximately to zero current. (Actually it does not go quite to zero current because of the curvature, but it goes to where zero current would be if the tube characteristics were all straight.) Using the same load line, the operating point for each tube would (in theory) be 400 volts at zero milliamperes. This means the plate potential voltage will swing from 100 volts to 700 volts. Plate current will swing, during one half-cycle, from zero to 60 milliamperes and back, while in the other half-cycle, no current flows in that tube.

The permissible maximum voltage on the plate is considerably increased by this method of operation (from 400 volts to 700 volts). There is less danger of breakdown between the plate and some other electrode when no plate current is flowing. There is, however, a maximum rated voltage even under this condition, which sometimes restricts the amount by which this method of operation can improve efficiency.

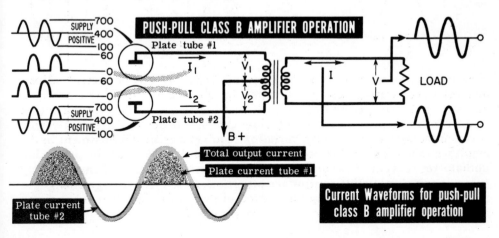

PUSH-PULL CLASS B AMPLIFIER OPERATION

Current Waveforms for push-pull class B amplifier operation

Class-B Operation (contd.)

In this case, the peak voltage and current swing are now 300 volts and 60 milliamperes in each direction, with one tube providing one half-wave and the other tube providing the other half-wave. This represents a peak power of (300 $\times$ .06) or 18 watts for the complete arrangement, or an average power of 9 watts—just double that of class-A push-pull operation.

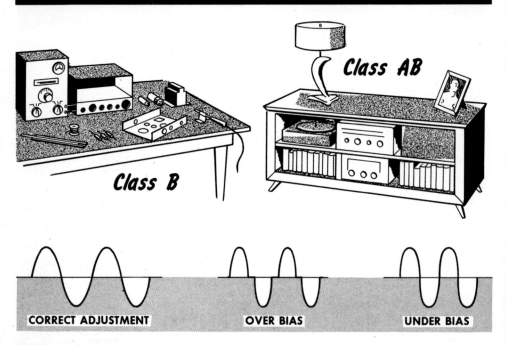

CLASS B OPERATION is suitable only where continuous skilled supervision is available

Class AB

Class B

CORRECT ADJUSTMENT   OVER BIAS   UNDER BIAS

This method is not too often used because it involves very careful adjustment of the operating point. Tubes vary in individual characteristics due to production differences, with the result that the zero plate current point (the point where the grid bias cuts off plate current) is apt to differ noticeably between individual tubes. This variation requires a critical adjustment in the amplifier to make sure that both tubes are at the correct point for producing undistorted output. Not only is this adjustment critical when replacing tubes, it can also involve continuous attention if the plate voltage changes at all due to line voltage supply fluctuation or due to the fact that tubes sometimes change their characteristics as they get older.

Class-AB Operation

Class-B operation is only really suitable for amplifiers where constant skilled attention is available to insure the conditions are correct. Most practical amplifiers are used under circumstances where they are installed and forgotten. A class-B amplifier would likely give considerable distortion if this were done.

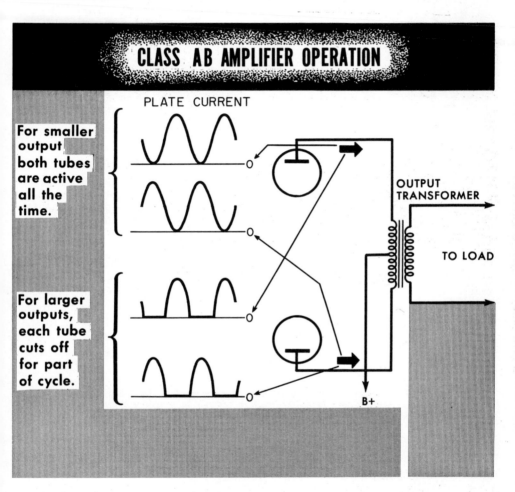

CLASS AB AMPLIFIER OPERATION

PLATE CURRENT

For smaller output both tubes are active all the time.

For larger outputs, each tube cuts off for part of cycle.

OUTPUT TRANSFORMER

TO LOAD

B+

For this reason a popular method (called class-AB) consists of splitting the difference. For small outputs, up to about half maximum power, both tubes are conducting current all of the time. When full output is needed, each tube goes beyond the zero plate current for part of the cycle, but for not a complete half-waveform. This design results in an amplifier that is less critical in operation and can be used without critical selection of output tubes and adjustment of bias.

Power Drive

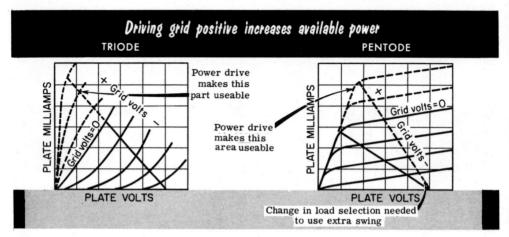

Driving grid positive increases available power

TRIODE

PENTODE

PLATE MILLIAMPS

Grid volts

Grid volts = O

Power drive makes this part useable

Power drive makes this area useable

PLATE VOLTS

PLATE VOLTS

Change in load selection needed to use extra swing

One more thing can be done to increase the power available from a given pair of tubes. If the control grid is made positive, the plate current will rise still farther, whether a tube is operated as a triode or pentode. In the case of pentode operation, the load value must be changed, otherwise additional grid swing into the positive cannot extend the *length* of the load line. This would still result in clipping that no amount of grid current could remedy.

Applying positive drive on the grid means that the grid itself will draw current when it becomes positive with respect to the cathode. (Some of the electrons will be attracted to the grid itself, instead of passing through it to the other electrodes.) This means that the grid is no longer just a voltage-operated electrode in the tube. We now have to make a more complicated design of the *drive stage,* as it is called, to provide the necessary grid current (when it is drawn) accompanying the correct voltage waveform, to give the right output.

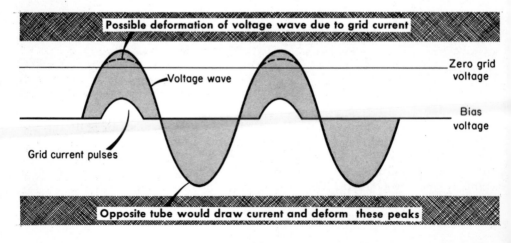

Possible deformation of voltage wave due to grid current

Voltage wave

Zero grid voltage

Bias voltage

Grid current pulses

Opposite tube would draw current and deform these peaks

Amplifier Efficiency and Distortion

We have a variety of circuits that can be used to get more power from tubes. Increasing the efficiency is in itself an advantage for many purposes, but it brings with it some disadvantages. Probably the best kind of output for general purpose use, if the inefficiency can be tolerated, is the push-pull triode-operated arrangement. It gives good clean amplification, whether the correct load value (according to design) is used, or a value that may differ from it by a ratio of 2:1 or more.

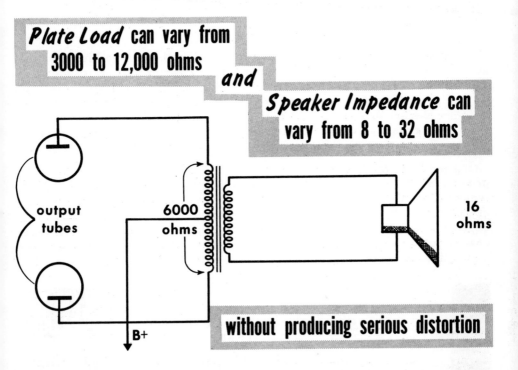

If, for example, the plate load of the two tubes in push-pull should be 6000 ohms, they will not show serious distortion if an actual plate load is used ranging from 3000 to 12,000 ohms, or even more. In terms of the secondary side of an output transformer designed to feed a 16-ohm loudspeaker, it will not produce serious distortion even if it is connected to an 8-ohm or 32-ohm loudspeaker.

Of course, using an incorrect load in this way will reduce the available output proportionally, but it does not in itself introduce distortion. The maximum rated output will only be given into the correct load but use of a different load does not seriously decrease the maximum output and, provided the amplifier is not run into overload conditions, it will not cause distortion.

Amplifier Efficiency and Distortion (contd.)

This kind of output requires two 25-watt type tubes, which are relatively large, and must dissipate 50 watts of heat in themselves to give a maximum audio output in the region of 6 or 7 watts. If the operating condition changes to class B, the output will be raised to 10 or 12 watts. With this change, the operation condition is more critical. The amplifier needs careful adjustment, but it does not usually introduce serious distortion by using the wrong load value, provided this is *higher* than the rated value. For example, if the rated secondary impedance of the output transformer is 16 ohms, this circuit will operate successfully with a loudspeaker rated at 32 ohms, but not with one rated at 8 ohms.

The use of pentode- or beam-tetrode-type tubes will considerably boost the available output. A pair of tubes dissipating 25 watts of heat each (a total of 50 watts) can give an audio output of as much as 30 watts. Using this kind of circuit and working into power drive (which means the grids of the output tubes are driven into the positive region at parts of the audio waveform), it is possible to push the power output of two 25-watt triodes working in class-B push-pull up to 50 watts.

Using pentodes this way can give as much as 100 watts from tubes that only produce 50 watts heat between them. The maximum audio output is thus twice as much as the heat generated in the tubes themselves. This is very useful for high-powered systems, but involves critical adjustment, more expensive supply circuits, and careful attention to see that the load value connected to the amplifier is correct. Otherwise, the power output quickly diminishes.

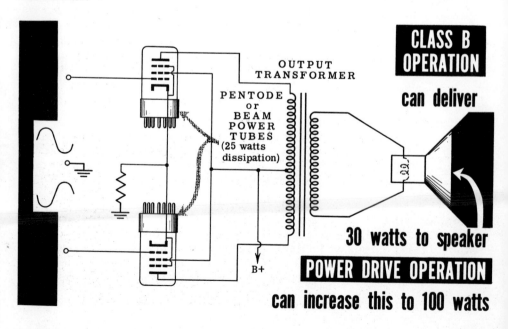

OUTPUT
TRANSFORMER

PENTODE
or
BEAM
POWER
TUBES
(25 watts
dissipation)

B+

CLASS B OPERATION can deliver

30 watts to speaker

POWER DRIVE OPERATION can increase this to 100 watts

Amplifier Efficiency and Distortion (contd.)

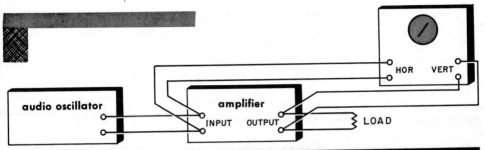

SCOPE TRACE IS A STRAIGHT SLOPING LINE IF OUTPUT IS ALWAYS A PROPORTIONATELY AMPLIFIED VERSION OF THE INPUT

What kind of thing happens when amplifiers are not correctly operated? We can see this using the oscilloscope to look at the waveforms. Possibly the most interesting way to do so from the viewpoint of what happens in the amplifier is to connect the input sine wave to the horizontal deflection plates and the output waveform to the vertical deflection plates, instead of using the sawtooth time base. This gives us what should be a straight sloping line on the screen.

If the line curves or squares off in any way, this shows distortion, because it means the output waveform is not following the input waveform in correct proportion. If an attempt is made to get too much power from an amplifier, this means that the grids of the output tubes will be driven positive (or in the case of output circuits designed to take positive grid drive, they will be driven *more* positive than they should be). The waveform flattens because an increase in fluctuation at the input is not accompanied by a corresponding increase in fluctuation at the output. If a load of an incorrect value is used with tubes that require careful selection of the load, the waveform will change its shape, getting either sharper or flatter towards the tips, or waving about in different ways.

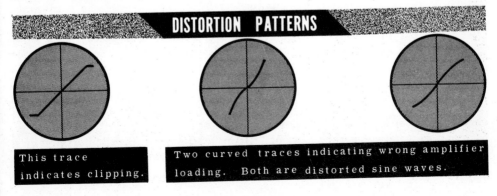

DISTORTION PATTERNS

This trace indicates clipping.

Two curved traces indicating wrong amplifier loading. Both are distorted sine waves.

Amplifier Efficiency and Distortion (contd.)

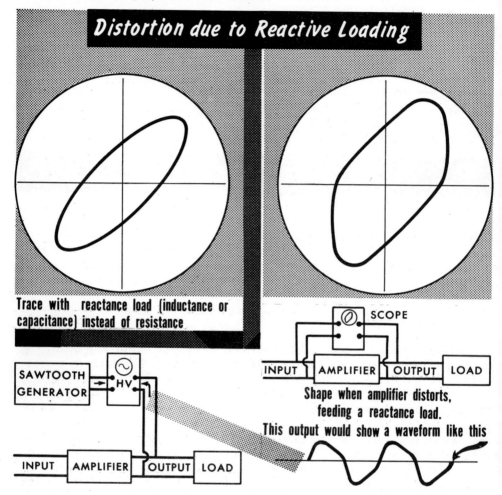

Distortion due to Reactive Loading

Trace with reactance load (inductance or capacitance) instead of resistance

SCOPE

INPUT | AMPLIFIER | OUTPUT | LOAD

Shape when amplifier distorts, feeding a reactance load. This output would show a waveform like this

SAWTOOTH GENERATOR → HV

INPUT | AMPLIFIER | OUTPUT | LOAD

With amplifiers in which the loading is important, trouble is sometimes caused because the load is not a pure resistance but possesses reactance in the form of inductance or capacitance along with the resistance. In a loud-speaker some of this reactance may be due to the inductance of the voice coil, whereas the resistive component is the d-c resistance of the coil. The actual working of the loudspeaker can cause additional components of resistance and reactance as well. Even if the total impedance of such a combination is the correct number of ohms, it may still cause distortion because the amplifier does not work well into a reactive load. This kind of distortion usually has the effect of "tilting" the waveform when viewed on a sawtooth timebase, or when viewed against the input, it opens out the slanting line trace into a distorted ellipse.

PHASE-SPLITTING CIRCUITS

The Transformer-Type Phase Splitter

We have talked about using tubes in push-pull and said that to do this we need to have an audio input that makes one grid fluctuate positively while the other one fluctuates negatively. The question now comes, "How can we get this kind of drive or audio voltage for push-pull output tubes?" There are a number of these so-called *phase-splitting circuits.*

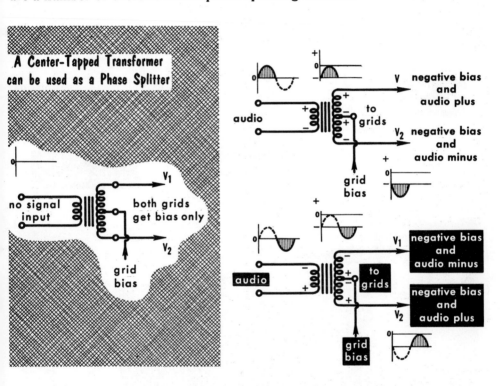

The simplest arrangement uses a variety of audio transformer similar to the output transformer. The secondary, however, has more turns than the primary and is center-tapped, like the primary winding of the push-pull output transformer. The center tap is connected to the negative grid bias voltage. When no audio is passing, both ends of the secondary winding have the negative grid bias voltage for their respective grids. When an audio voltage is presented to the primary of the transformer, one end of the winding goes positive from the bias voltage while the other one goes negative, and vice versa.

This system has some very useful features. It is simple, and it gives good balance in voltages supplied to each grid, if it is well designed. It has, however, a disadvantage when used in a feedback amplifier, as will be explained later, and for this reason various phase-splitting circuits that do not employ transformers or chokes are preferred in modern amplifiers.

(2-87)

The Split-Load Circuit

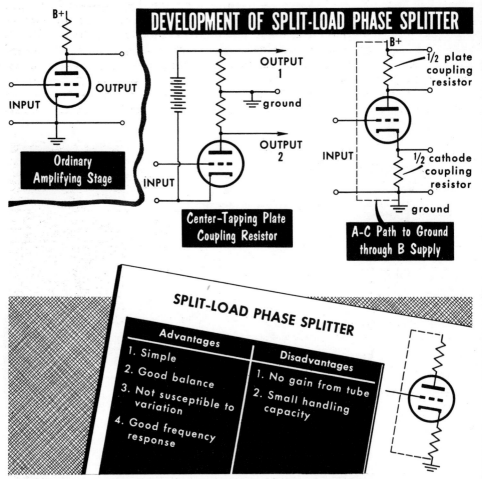

DEVELOPMENT OF SPLIT-LOAD PHASE SPLITTER

Ordinary Amplifying Stage

Center-Tapping Plate Coupling Resistor

½ plate coupling resistor
½ cathode coupling resistor
A-C Path to Ground through B Supply

SPLIT-LOAD PHASE SPLITTER

Advantages	Disadvantages
1. Simple	1. No gain from tube
2. Good balance	2. Small handling capacity
3. Not susceptible to variation	
4. Good frequency response	

One simple way to make a phase splitter is to connect half of the plate load resistance between B+ and plate and the other half between cathode and ground. Since these resistances are equal and the same current flows through both, each will produce the same d-c voltage drop and the same audio fluctuations. When the fluctuation across the plate resistor goes positive, due to decrease in plate current, this same fluctuation will be negative across the cathode connected resistor because of the same decrease in current. This provides voltages of opposite phase, but we still must provide input to the tubes. The normal place to apply input voltage to a tube is between the grid and cathode, however, in this arrangement, half the total output voltage is between cathode and ground. This circuit uses the tube just to get phase *inversion* (to reverse the voltage between grid and plate) and does not achieve any useful amplification.

The Split-Load Circuit (contd.)

Using one-half of the 12AU7 as an example, an input fluctuation of 10 volts, measured between grid and *cathode*, will produce an output fluctuation of 100 volts—50 volts at the plate and 50 volts at the cathode. When the grid-to-cathode voltage goes 5 volts positive from its bias point, the current through the tube will increase. The cathode will go 25 volts positive from its d-c operating point, while the plate will go 25 volts negative from the d-c operating point. As the cathode has now gone 25 volts *more* positive from ground, and the grid-to-*cathode* voltage needs to go 5 volts positive to *cause*

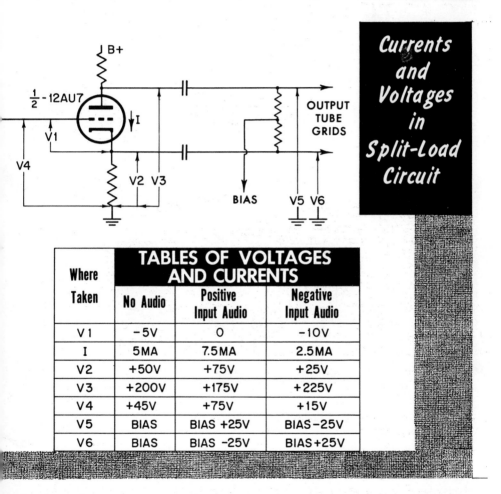

Currents and Voltages in Split-Load Circuit

Where	TABLES OF VOLTAGES AND CURRENTS		
Taken	No Audio	Positive Input Audio	Negative Input Audio
V1	−5V	0	−10V
I	5MA	7.5MA	2.5MA
V2	+50V	+75V	+25V
V3	+200V	+175V	+225V
V4	+45V	+75V	+15V
V5	BIAS	BIAS +25V	BIAS −25V
V6	BIAS	BIAS −25V	BIAS +25V

this, the grid-to-ground voltage itself must go 25 + 5, or 30 volts more positive to produce this swing. We therefore require a 60-volt peak-to-peak audio fluctuation from grid to *ground* to produce a 50-volt peak-to-peak fluctuation at plate and cathode, respectively.

The Paraphase Circuit

Another phase-splitting arrangement is the so-called *paraphase* circuit. It uses two tubes. The output from the plate of one tube is fed by R-C coupling to the grid of one of the output tubes. From this same point, a voltage-divider arrangement cuts down the voltage and applies it to the grid of a second tube, which amplifies the voltage by as much as the resistance divider cuts it down, producing a voltage for driving the second output tube.

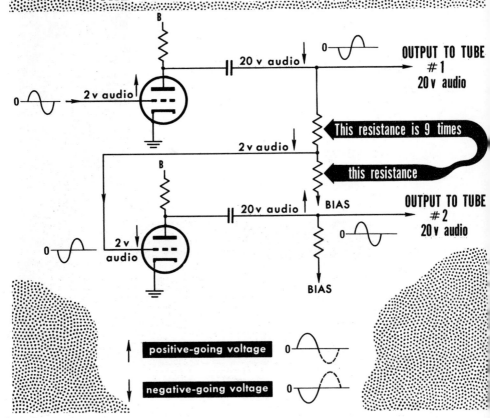

THE PARAPHASE CIRCUIT ACTION

A positive fluctuation of 2 volts at the grid of the first paraphase tube produces a negative fluctuation at its plate of, say, 20 volts, which appears at the grid of one of the output tubes. This 20-volt fluctuation is also divided to provide a negative fluctuation of 2 volts for the grid of the second paraphase tube and becomes a positive fluctuation of 20 volts at the plate, providing positive fluctuation for the grid of the second output tube.

The Paraphase Circuit (contd.)

Paraphase Circuit and Characteristics
Paraphase Phase Splitter

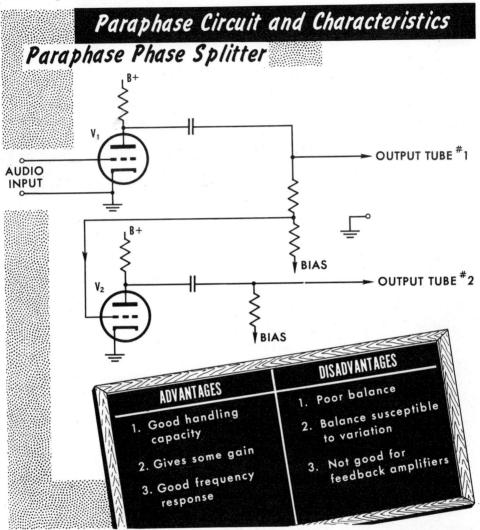

ADVANTAGES	DISADVANTAGES
1. Good handling capacity	1. Poor balance
2. Gives some gain	2. Balance susceptible to variation
3. Good frequency response	3. Not good for feedback amplifiers

For this circuit to operate correctly, the voltage division produced by the resistors feeding the second tube must be exactly in the same ratio as the gain provided by the second tube. In the example given, the tube is multiplied by ten, and the voltage divider divided by ten. As tubes are subject to variation with line voltage, individual samples from production, and other differences, there is no guarantee that the amplification provided by the tube will be exactly the same as the voltage division provided by the resistors. The tube may amplify 9 or 11 times. Consequently this circuit is subject to deviation in its accuracy in a way that the two circuits discussed earlier were not.

The Floating Paraphase Circuit

The next circuit aims at overcoming this problem. It is called *floating para-phase*. Instead of using a fixed voltage divider, the voltage divider is arranged to have a self-adjusting action that overcomes, to some extent, possible differences between individual tubes or changes in operating conditions. Instead of using a large resistor and a small resistor, as employed in the paraphase circuit, the tapping point used for connecting to the grid of the second paraphase tube is a junction point of large resistors from the output-tube grids and a third resistor from the bias point.

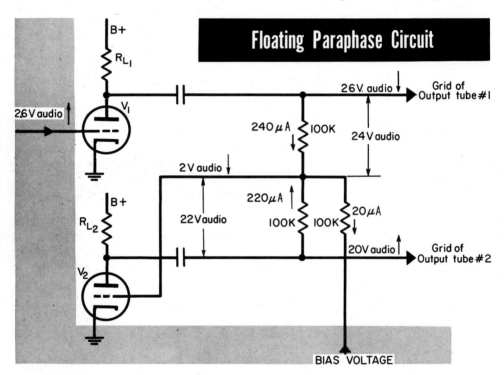

Assume that the three resistors have the same value, 100,000 ohms, and that the tubes have a gain of 10, as before. For the second tube to get its 2-volt grid fluctuation, the current through the common resistor must be 2/100,000 or 20 microamperes. The voltage at the grid of the second output tube will fluctuate 20 volts in the opposite direction, hence the resistor connecting this grid to the common point will have 22 volts across it and pass 220 microamperes. Because the resistor from the first output-tube grid joins this same point, it must have 220 + 20 or 240 microamperes flowing in it, which will produce a fluctuation voltage across it of 24 volts. As the common point is already fluctuating 2 volts in this direction, the total fluctuation at the first output tube grid must be 26 volts.

The Floating Paraphase Circuit (contd.)

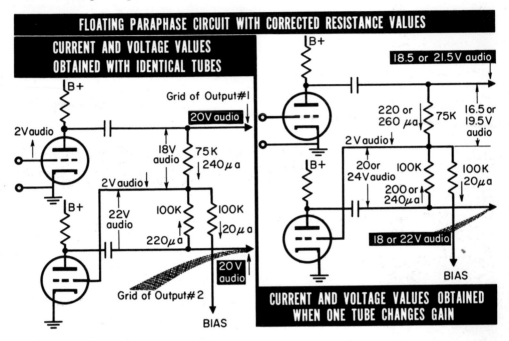

FLOATING PARAPHASE CIRCUIT WITH CORRECTED RESISTANCE VALUES

The unbalance between output tube grids can be corrected by using a smaller resistance value from the first output tube, so that 240 microamps only drop 18 volts. This requires a resistor of $18/0.00024 = 75,000$ ohms, in place of 100,000 ohms.

Now what happens if the second tube changes gain to either 9 or 11? If it still gets 2 volts on its grid, there will be either 18 or 22 volts fluctuation at its plate, so the current in the resistor from the second output tube grid to the common point will be either 200 or 240 microamperes. The current in the resistor from the other output tube grid will need to be 220 or 260 microamps, instead of the original 240 microamps. This means that the potential at that grid will be $(75,000 \times .00022)$ or 16.5 volts, or $(75,000 \times .00026)$ or 19.5 volts, from the grid to the common point. This represents 18.5 or 21.5 volts total fluctuation at this grid, to compare with 18 or 22 volts at the other grid.

With the ordinary paraphase, the grid of the first output tube would remain at a potential of 20 volts, while the second output tube would get 18 or 22 volts. Here, when the second tube gets 18 volts, the first has 18.5 volts; when the second gets 22 volts, the first gets 21.5 volts, which reduces the imbalance. If the first grid continued to get 20 volts, the second grid would get within 19.5 to 20.5 volts with this much change in gain, instead of 18 or 22 volts with ordinary paraphase.

The Long-Tail Circuit

Another variation puts the common resistor that carries the plate current of both tubes in the circuit between cathode and ground. The input voltage to the second tube is the audio voltage developed across this common resistor, because the second tube grid is connected to ground either directly or through a large capacitor.

It doesn't matter which way we measure a voltage, whether from grid to cathode or cathode to grid. In either case it will be the same *voltage,* different only in polarity or phase. Hence the grid voltage for the second tube will be due to the difference in the audio components of plate current in the common cathode resistor. This means that the audio plate current of the first tube must be a little higher than the corresponding component of the second tube. If identical plate resistors are used, the first tube will produce a slightly greater audio voltage than the second tube. This can again be overcome by using plate resistors of different values so that the audio voltages become equal.

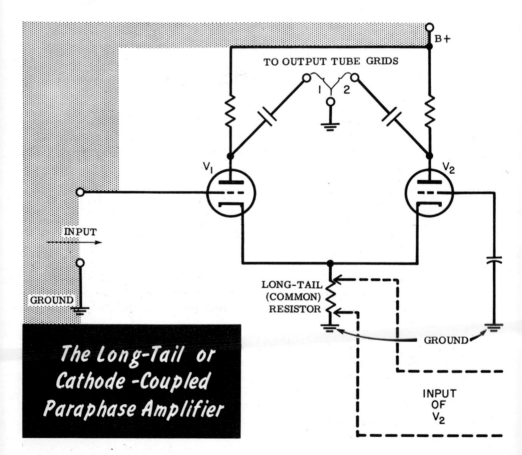

QUESTIONS AND PROBLEMS

1. What are the advantages of working tubes in push-pull?

2. Explain how using tubes in push-pull enables them to be used (a) with less distortion, (b) to give more power (higher efficiency)?

3. Give the relative advantages of operating tubes in (a) class A, (b) class B, (c) class AB.

4. What is power drive, and how does it alter the requirements of the preceding stage?

5. What is the most informative way of displaying the distortion performance of an amplifier using an oscilloscope?

6. What is a phase splitter and when is it needed? Discuss the relative features of the following different types, with special reference for each to (a) accuracy of the two outputs, (b) uniformity of performance at different frequencies, (c) economical use of components:
    (i) Transformer type
    (ii) Split-load type
    (iii) Paraphase type
    (iv) Floating paraphase type
    (v) Long-tail type
    (vi) Paraphase from output transformer.

7. Compare different output circuits, using triode or pentode tubes, in various classes of operation, with regard to the power output that can be obtained for a given dissipation rating, to probable distortion content, to critical load requirements, and to the requirement of critical adjustment in operation.

8. In spite of the fact that it is evidently a good phase-splitting device, the transformer is very seldom used in modern amplifiers. Why?

9. The split-load circuit is criticized for not having any useful gain. Explain why this is. Why is its handling capacity less than some other types?

10. Describe, with numerical illustration to prove your point, why the floating paraphase maintains betters balance than the simple paraphase circuit.

11. In a floating paraphase circuit, the section of grid resistor common to both output tubes has one-half the average value of the other two, which are slightly unequal, so that when the gain of the phase-splitting tube is 20, both output tubes get equal drive. Using values to illustrate this condition, find how much error will result from the phase-splitter tube's losing working gain down to 15.

AUDIO TRANSFORMERS

Review of Transformer Action

Audio transformers are used to match one circuit to another. For an ideal transformer, the ratio of the primary and secondary voltages varies directly with the ratio of the number of turns in the two windings, the ratio of primary and secondary current varies inversely with the turns ratio, and the primary and secondary impedance varies directly with the square of the turns ratio.

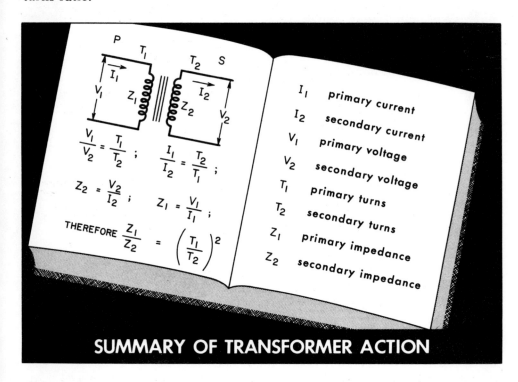

$$\frac{V_1}{V_2} = \frac{T_1}{T_2} \; ; \qquad \frac{I_1}{I_2} = \frac{T_2}{T_1} \; ;$$

$$Z_2 = \frac{V_2}{I_2} \; ; \qquad Z_1 = \frac{V_1}{I_1} \; ;$$

$$\text{THEREFORE } \frac{Z_1}{Z_2} = \left(\frac{T_1}{T_2}\right)^2$$

I_1 primary current

I_2 secondary current

V_1 primary voltage

V_2 secondary voltage

T_1 primary turns

T_2 secondary turns

Z_1 primary impedance

Z_2 secondary impedance

SUMMARY OF TRANSFORMER ACTION

These relationships may be explained as follows: the first two arise from the fact that (in an ideal transformer) the magnetization (measured in ampere-turns) of the core is zero at all times. If current is drawn from the secondary, the product of this current and the number of secondary turns must be cancelled by the product of an equal and opposite product of primary current and the number of primary turns. Since the ideal transformer neither adds nor absorbs power, the product of the primary voltage and current must equal the product of the secondary voltage and current. Thus current varies inversely with the turns ratio and voltage varies inversely with current or directly with the turns ratio. Since the secondary impedance is measured by the ratio of secondary voltage to secondary current, and the voltage has *increased* by the turns ratio while the current has *decreased* by the turns ratio, the impedance must change by the square of turns ratio.

Core Losses

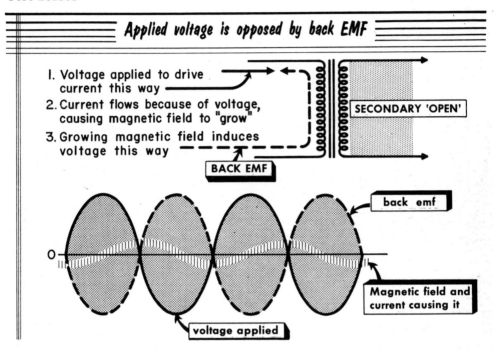

Applied voltage is opposed by back EMF

1. Voltage applied to drive current this way
2. Current flows because of voltage, causing magnetic field to "grow"
3. Growing magnetic field induces voltage this way

BACK EMF

SECONDARY 'OPEN'

back emf

Magnetic field and current causing it

voltage applied

Real transformers are not the same as ideal ones, however. Some current flows in the primary even when no secondary current flows. This current induces a voltage *(back emf)* in the primary that opposes the applied voltage. This opposing voltage prevents the flow of excessive current in the low-resistance primary and, since the magnetization of the core depends on the *current* in the windings, it limits core magnetization as well. It is because the back emf does not completely cancel the applied voltage that primary current flows in a real transformer. In a properly designed transformer, this current is quite small, but it represents loss that can be visualized as a resistor connected across the primary that acts in addition to the resistance referred from the secondary load.

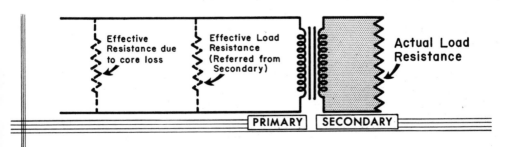

Effective Resistance due to core loss

Effective Load Resistance (Referred from Secondary)

Actual Load Resistance

PRIMARY   SECONDARY

Back Emf and Saturation

The magnitude of the back emf developed in the primary by an applied a-c voltage varies with the rate at which the current developed by the voltage changes. The more rapidly this current changes, the greater the back emf produced. The property of the primary that relates the rate of change of the current in the primary windings to the resultant back emf is known as the *primary inductance.* When the primary inductance is high, the back emf is high, and the magnetizing current is small.

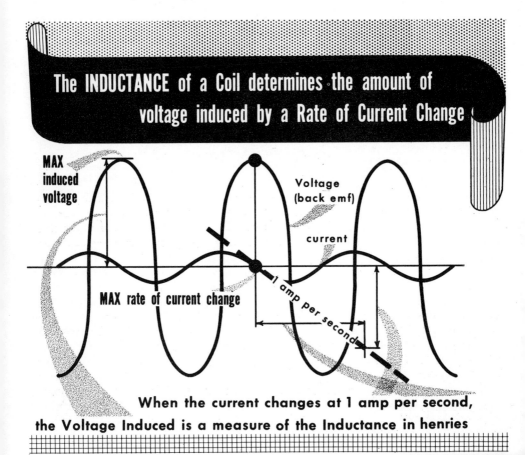

The INDUCTANCE of a Coil determines the amount of voltage induced by a Rate of Current Change

MAX induced voltage

Voltage (back emf)

current

MAX rate of current change

1 amp per second

When the current changes at 1 amp per second, the Voltage Induced is a measure of the Inductance in henries

There is a limit to the magnetization that a core can take, called *saturation.* Below this point, the primary inductance remains nearly constant and is relatively high. When saturation occurs, the relation between voltage induced and the further increase in current needed to produce it ceases to be approximately constant. It is as if the magnetic material disappeared and we had only an air-core inductor.

The Effect of Saturation

Saturation begins at a specific magnetization density. The back emf produced by this density depends on frequency, being directly proportional to it. This means that the power-handling capacity of a transformer is approximately proportional to the square of frequency. It is not a constant figure! Below saturation the relation between voltage and magnetizing current approximates that of simple inductance. Above the point on the current wave where saturation occurs, the current peaks up rapidly.

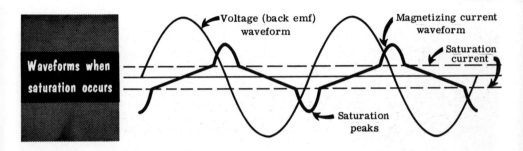

If the primary of the transformer were connected to a source of voltage having zero resistance, the sudden rise in magnetizing current due to saturation would make no difference. Drawing this heavy current from a voltage source that possesses internal resistance, however, causes a voltage drop coincident with the current peaks, distorting the primary voltage waveform as well.

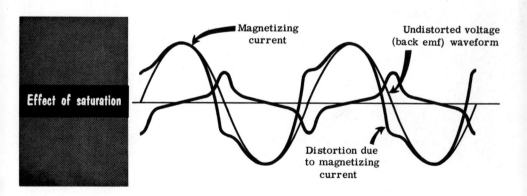

Frequency response below saturation is controlled by the relationship between primary inductance and the associated source and local resistances. Regardless of the saturation point, however, primary inductance causes a low-frequency loss at all voltage levels.

The Use of an Air Gap

With a good transformer core, very little current is needed to produce saturation. This means that passing the plate current through the primary winding will saturate the core unless some means is used to prevent it. Usually, an air gap is used for this purpose. It very considerably reduces the magnetization produced by any current in the primary winding, but it also reduces the primary inductance. The air gap has to be adjusted so that its effect in avoiding saturation is better than its effect in reducing primary inductance.

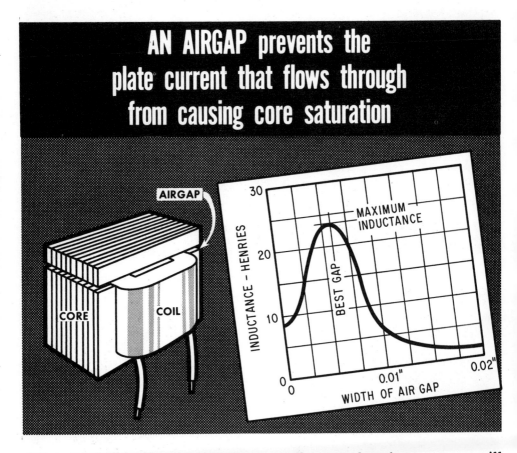

AN AIRGAP prevents the plate current that flows through from causing core saturation

Using too small an air gap, or no air gap at all, means the primary current will cause the core to saturate and thus the inductance will practically disappear. Using too large an air gap amounts to making the transformer almost air cored, which again will result in a very low inductance. There is always an optimum size for the air gap, which will result in the biggest practical value of inductance for a transformer that carries direct current in one of its windings.

Other Losses

Primary inductance and core losses, together with distortion, are the principal things that complicate the behavior of an audio transformer at low frequencies. At high frequencies the behavior of the transformer is complicated by winding capacitance and leakage inductance. Winding capacitance allows minute audio currents to pass between points of audio voltage where there is no direct connection, in the way that stray capacitance allows audio current to pass at extremely high frequencies.

The magnetic field causing primary inductance follows a path through the magnetic core that embraces both windings. The current in the windings themselves, however, induces a magnetic field around each winding (apart from the bigger one in the core) that tends to "leak down" between the two windings. This means that the current in one winding will not produce a field that counter-balances the current in the other winding. Consequently, these uncounterbalanced fields will produce different voltages in their respective windings. Thus *leakage inductance* is like an inductance in series with the winding, because it allows an additional voltage to be developed between the terminals that is not accounted for by the counter-balancing effect of current in the two windings.

A well-designed audio transformer has to take into account all of these factors to make sure that its performance as an impedance-matching device is consistent over the frequency range for which it is intended.

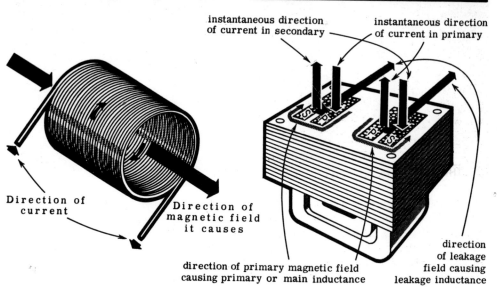

Ordinary Inductance

Direction of current

Direction of magnetic field it causes

Leakage Inductance

instantaneous direction of current in secondary

instantaneous direction of current in primary

direction of primary magnetic field causing primary or main inductance

direction of leakage field causing leakage inductance

Input and Interstage Transformers

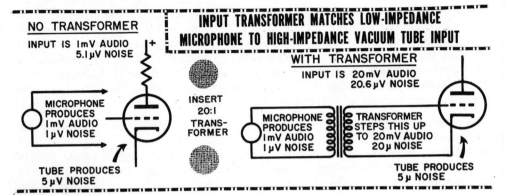

Audio transformers are used where the impedance is not naturally what is needed for best performance. For low-impedance pickups or microphones working into tube grids, the transformer steps up the minute voltages (in this case impedance is incidental) to achieve better margin over tube noise. Sometimes interstage transformers are used for essentially the same purpose. The limit to what can be done occurs when the impedance connected to the primary is stepped up to such a value that it adversely affects performance in some other way.

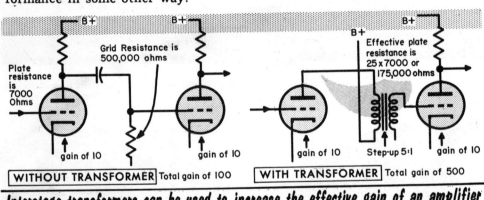

Interstage transformers can be used to increase the effective gain of an amplifier

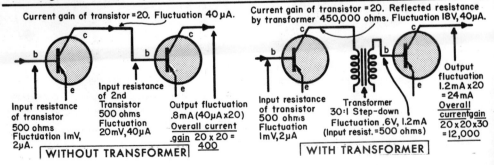

Drive Transformers

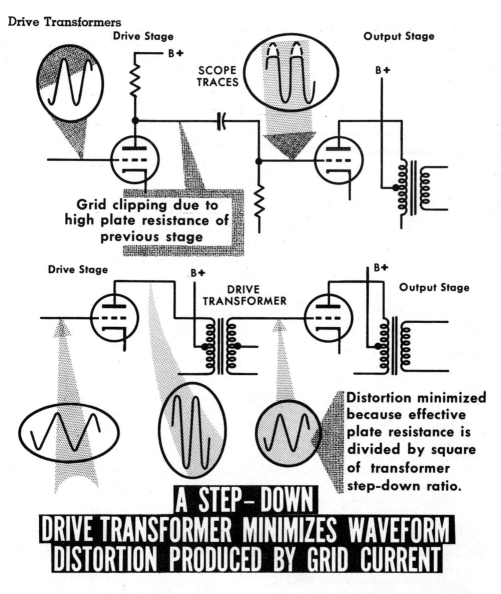

Grid clipping due to high plate resistance of previous stage

Distortion minimized because effective plate resistance is divided by square of transformer step-down ratio.

A STEP-DOWN DRIVE TRANSFORMER MINIMIZES WAVEFORM DISTORTION PRODUCED BY GRID CURRENT

Step-down transformers can also be used in the drive stage that feeds a push-pull output stage, where the grids of the output tubes are driven into the positive voltage region during part of the audio waveform. This means there will be current peaks which tend to distort the audio voltage at the grid, caused by a drop in the high source resistance (usually the plate resistance of the preceding stage). The apparent source resistance can be reduced down by a step-down drive transformer, which thus minimizes the waveform distortion produced by the grid current.

AUDIO TRANSFORMERS

Output Transformers

The most common form of audio transformer is used in the output of an amplifier to match the actual load impedance (usually that of a loudspeaker) to that required by the output tubes. The transformer here serves the additional purpose of avoiding both supply and audio losses because the winding resistances are low compared to their respective impedances. The way impedance reflects in a push-pull transformer depends to some extent on the way tubes are operated. In class A, both tubes are delivering part of the power throughout the cycle, so the load is shared between them. If the ratio make 16 ohms actual impedance equivalent to 6400 ohms at the primary, each tube has a load of 3200 ohms average.

But in class B, only one-half of the primary works at a time. The other is inactive for that half-cycle because its tube is cut off. Consequently the impedance transformation is based on the ratio to each half-winding. If the whole ratio is 20:1, this is 10:1 each half. So 16 ohms connected to the secondary makes a load of 1600 ohms for each tube, but the tube takes the load for only half a cycle.

A further advantage of push-pull operation in the transformer is that the magnetizing effect due to steady plate current cancels, whether the tubes are operated class A or class B. This means that no air gap is necessary to prevent saturation. In turn, this allows a much smaller core to be used for providing an adequate primary inductance with the available turns in the primary winding.

Of particular importance in output transformers is the leakage inductance between windings. Due to the load current in both windings, the leakage flux induces a voltage difference between the ideal ratio and what you might actually measure. Being an inductance, this voltage difference becomes larger with higher frequency. Its effect is to "uncouple" the load from the tubes at these higher frequencies, resulting in high-frequency loss. This uncoupling effect of the leakage inductance is like connecting an inductance in series with the load impedance.

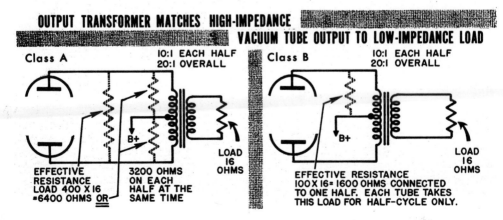

OUTPUT TRANSFORMER MATCHES HIGH-IMPEDANCE VACUUM TUBE OUTPUT TO LOW-IMPEDANCE LOAD

Class A — 10:1 EACH HALF 20:1 OVERALL

EFFECTIVE RESISTANCE LOAD 400 X 16 =6400 OHMS OR — 3200 OHMS ON EACH HALF AT THE SAME TIME — B+ — LOAD 16 OHMS

Class B — 10:1 EACH HALF 20:1 OVERALL

EFFECTIVE RESISTANCE 100 X 16= 1600 OHMS CONNECTED TO ONE HALF. EACH TUBE TAKES THIS LOAD FOR HALF-CYCLE ONLY. — B+ — LOAD 16 OHMS

DISTORTION

Harmonic Distortion

The basic purpose of an amplifier is to amplify the audio input voltages without distorting them in any way. The output audio voltage should be an *exact* replica of the input voltage, except that it is very much larger—1000 or even a greater number of times. Practical amplifiers never *completely* achieve this exactness, although they may get very close to it. There is always some distortion that makes the output waveform a trifle different from the input waveform.

When the word distortion is used without qualification, it is usually taken to mean the kind of distortion due to curved or nonlinear characteristics in the amplifier. The fact that a change in audio voltage at the input is not accompanied by an exactly corresponding change at the output, at different points on the waveform is a form of distortion.

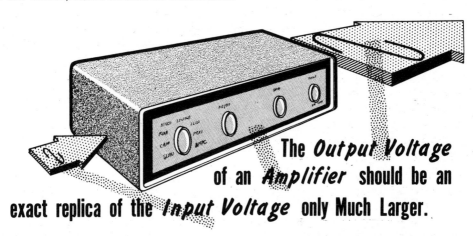

The *Output Voltage* of an *Amplifier* should be an exact replica of the *Input Voltage* only Much Larger.

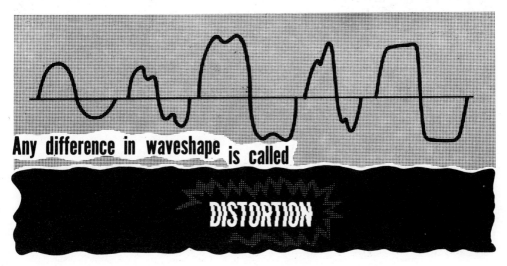

Any difference in waveshape is called

DISTORTION

Harmonic Distortion (contd.)

Distortion due to 2nd or even-numbered harmonics

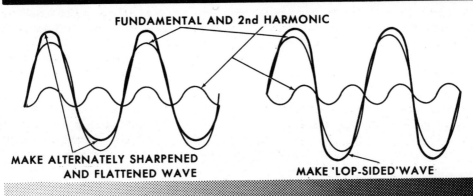

FUNDAMENTAL AND 2nd HARMONIC

MAKE ALTERNATELY SHARPENED
AND FLATTENED WAVE

MAKE 'LOP-SIDED' WAVE

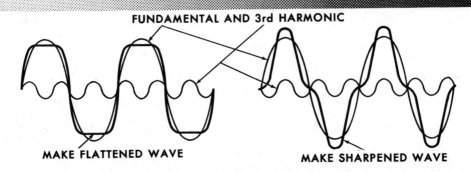

FUNDAMENTAL AND 3rd HARMONIC

MAKE FLATTENED WAVE

MAKE SHARPENED WAVE

Distortion due to 3rd or odd-numbered harmonics

If we consider what this kind of curvature does to the amplification of a wave of single frequency, we can see how it introduces harmonic distortion —the presence of overtones of the fundamental frequency that are not present at the input.

A sharpening or flattening of both tops and bottoms of the waves is equivalent to the addition of third or other odd-numbered harmonics of the original frequency. A flattening at one peak and a sharpening at the other is equivalent to the addition of second and other even-numbered harmonics of the original frequency. If the waveform goes lopsided, that is, the upward slope is different from the downward slope, this is also due to second or other even-numbered harmonics added to the original frequency.

These are the principal kinds of harmonic distortion. Any real example will usually consist of one or a combination of two or more of them.

DISTORTION

Measurement of Harmonic Distortion

The presence of these harmonics can be measured by using a *wave analyzer*. It is quite a complicated and expensive piece of measuring equipment that has a frequency selective amplifier that permits it to measure the amplitude of any particular frequency in a composite output waveform. By setting the frequency dial first to the fundamental frequency of a pure sinusoidal input and then to successive harmonics, the component of each harmonic in the output waveform can be measured to find out how much total distortion is produced.

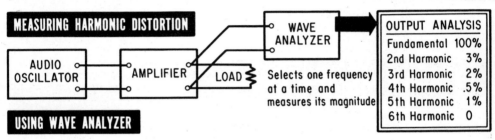

The use of the wave analyzer is rather a long-winded method, so a simple distortion measuring set is usually used to give the answer quite quickly. This method uses another kind of frequency-selective filter to eliminate the fundamental. Two positions are provided on the switch: one for measuring the amount of fundamental and the other for measuring the total amount of audio after the fundamental has been removed. This gives a quick and ready means of measuring the total distortion.

In the early days of audio amplifiers 5% harmonic was considered a good figure of distortion. At that time, tests were made which showed that human hearing could barely detect 5% of second harmonic. If the distortion is third harmonic, about 1.5% is just audible. At higher harmonics lower percentages become audible. Modern amplifiers produce harmonic distortion figures that are a fraction of 1%. According to the tests just described, this distortion should be completely inaudible.

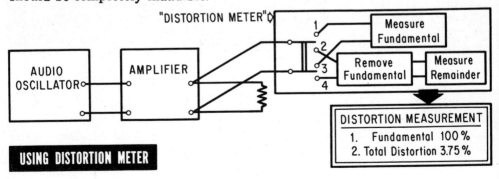

DISTORTION

Intermodulation Distortion

Low percentages of harmonic distortion may be inaudible, as such, but the same curvature in the amplifier characteristics causes another kind of distortion, called *intermodulation distortion* (IM for short). The effects of this kind of distortion can be audible when the harmonic distortion is not. There are two basic kinds of intermodulation distortion.

The first kind occurs because the amplification changes during a wave as well as introducing harmonics of this wave. This change in amplification will modulate or change the amplification of higher frequencies present in the same composite audio wave and this modulation of the higher frequencies is what becomes audible.

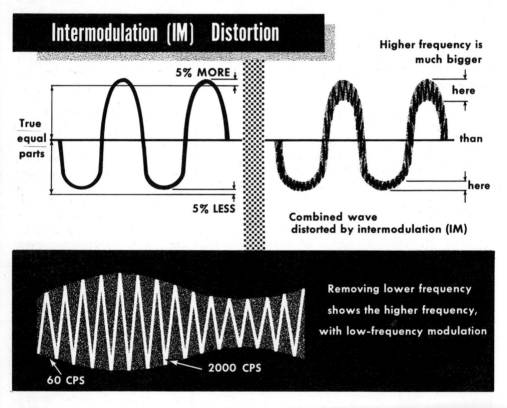

Suppose that a 60-cycle wave has 5% of second harmonic. This will mean one-half of the wave will get amplified by 5% more, while the other is amplified by 5% less. If the amplifier is also called upon to handle a 2000-cycle wave of much smaller magnitude than the 60-cycle wave, this will also get amplified by 5% more on one peak of the 60-cycle wave than it does on the other peak of the 60-cycle wave. Thus the 2000-cycle wave will be fluctuating in amplitude at the rate of 60 cycles.

Intermodulation Distortion (contd.)

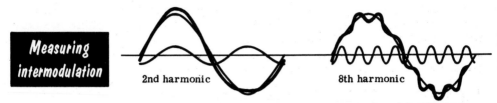

Measuring intermodulation

2nd harmonic   8th harmonic

Both harmonics are same magnitude, but the higher numbered one has much bigger effect on the shape of the combined waveform.

This effect on the 2000-cycle tone is quite audible as a dithery modulation of the tone. It is often noticed in organ music accompanying deep bass tones. If the curvature in the amplifier is of a kind that produces higher numbered harmonics than second or third, it will also produce increasing amounts of intermodulation because the smaller amount of higher frequencies added to the basic fundamental tone produce more noticeable changes in the waveform.

This kind of intermodulation distortion is measured by using two tones, usually a combined audio voltage at two frequencies, such as 60 and 2000 cycles, with the voltage at 60 cycles 4 times that at 2000 cycles. The combined waveform is fed into the amplifier and a special distortion measuring set applied to the output waveform. First the waveform is fed through a filter that removes the 60-cycle component completely. This leaves the 2000-cycle component which fluctuates in amplitude if intermodulation is present. This 2000-cycle waveform is then rectified, which gives a d-c output with the fluctuation riding on it. The d-c component can now be readily removed by passing the wave through a blocking capacitor, and the fluctuation is measured as an audio voltage. By careful calibration of the whole setup the amount of fluctuation at the output can be measured as a percentage of the total output waveform.

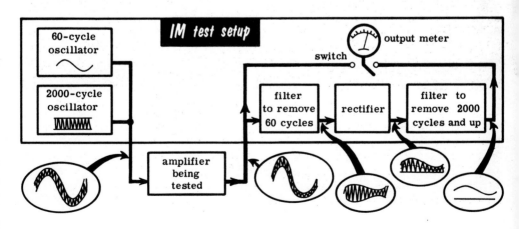

Intermodulation Distortion (contd.)

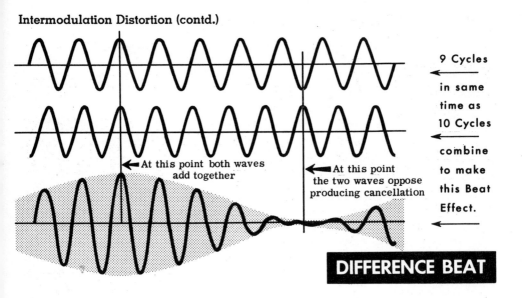

At this point both waves add together

At this point the two waves oppose producing cancellation

9 Cycles in same time as 10 Cycles combine to make this Beat Effect.

DIFFERENCE BEAT

The second kind of intermodulation distortion is caused by two relatively high frequencies producing a combined tone at a lower frequency. If two frequencies are very nearly the same, the combined waveform will gradually move in and out of phase at a rate dependent on the difference between the two frequencies. At one point, the two frequencies will add, producing a double amplitude, while at a point a little later, the two frequencies will subtract, giving an amplitude which is the difference between the individual amplitudes.

If this combination is applied to an amplifier without distortion, the waveform will be faithfully reproduced as would any other waveform. If the amplifier introduces any asymmetrical distortion, however, the upper part, at the peak in the combined waveform due to addition of the two components, will be amplified more than the lower part of the same peaks. This is equivalent to adding a component of the low frequency corresponding to the difference between the individual test frequencies.

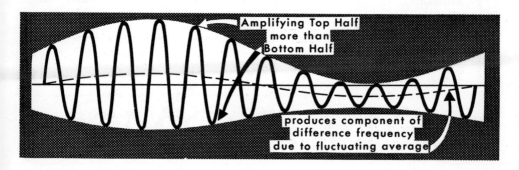

Amplifying Top Half more than Bottom Half

produces component of difference frequency due to fluctuating average

Intermodulation Distortion (contd.)

Suppose one of the frequencies is 4000 cycles and the other one 4200 cycles; the difference frequency is 200 cycles, which is quite clearly audible and of a frequency so different from the original frequencies that quite a small percentage of distortion becomes audible.

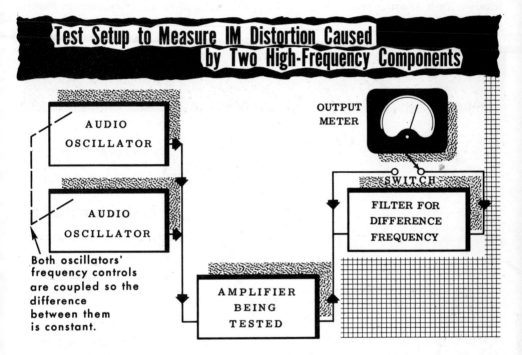

The method of testing for this kind of distortion is to use two oscillators that generate audio frequencies differing by a fixed amount. For example, if we decide to use the 200-cycle difference frequncy, we would arrange that one oscillator give 4000 cycles and the other one 4200 cycles. Or, to test at a higher frequency, when one oscillator gives 8000 cycles the other must give 8200 cycles. The output from the amplifier is passed through a filter that rejects the high frequencies and picks out any component at 200 cycles.

The problem with this method of measurement is that it only discovers whether there is any distortion due to the curvature that would cause *second* harmonic distortion. Other kinds of curvature will also produce distortion, but will not result in a simple 200-cycle difference tone. Rather, they will cause all sorts of other unwanted tones. For this reason and others too complicated to give a complete explanation, the results of the two methods of intermodulation test and harmonic measurement are not consistent, but they depend on the amount of different kinds of curvature in the amplification characteristic of the amplifier.

DISTORTION

Frequency Response

Amplifiers produce another kind of distortion because they do not amplify all frequencies uniformly (by the same amount). Low frequencies are reduced in amplitude by the effect of coupling capacitors. Various stray capacitances and the leakage inductance in the output transformer result in loss of high frequencies. Thus no amplifier amplifies all frequencies absolutely uniformly.

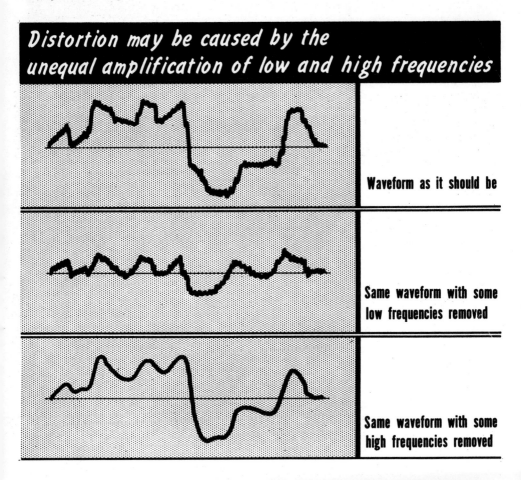

Distortion may be caused by the unequal amplification of low and high frequencies

Waveform as it should be

Same waveform with some low frequencies removed

Same waveform with some high frequencies removed

While this non-uniformity does not result in the introduction of any spurious or unwanted frequencies, it does result in the change of the relative magnitude of different frequencies in a composite audio waveform. The frequencies in the middle of the band will usually be amplified more than the extremely low or extremely high frequencies and this will cause a change in the resultant waveform. Fortunately the difference in amplification over the audio range in modern amplifiers is extremely small.

Frequency Response (contd.)

This form of distortion can readily be measured by taking frequency-response measurements of the amplifier. Audio voltages are fed into the amplifier at different frequencies, from the lowest to the highest, and the output voltage is carefully measured to see how closely it corresponds with the input voltage. If an input of 1 millivolt at 1000 cycles produces an output of 10 volts, then 1 millivolt is applied to the amplifier at all frequencies from 20 cycles up to 20,000 cycles and the output voltage is also measured. This will deviate up or down from 10 volts, according to the frequency response of the amplifier. The measurements are usually converted into db according to the ratio of the actual output voltage to the 10-volt output that should be there.

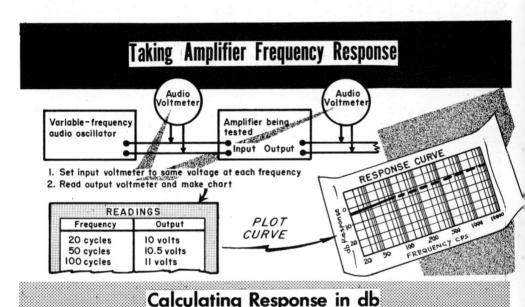

Taking Amplifier Frequency Response

Variable-frequency audio oscillator — Audio Voltmeter — Amplifier being tested (Input Output) — Audio Voltmeter

1. Set input voltmeter to same voltage at each frequency
2. Read output voltmeter and make chart

READINGS	
Frequency	Output
20 cycles	10 volts
50 cycles	10.5 volts
100 cycles	11 volts

PLOT CURVE

RESPONSE CURVE

Calculating Response in db

Output at 1000 cycles = 12V.
Output at 100 cycles = 11V.   Ratio = $\frac{12}{11}$ = 1.091

DECIBEL TABLE	
Voltage Ratio	Decibels
1.0	0.
1.091	.75
1.1	.828
1.2	1.584
1.3	2.279

■ Interpolate from table

Therefore response is down .75 db at 100 cycles.

DISTORTION

Amplifier Specifications

A good amplifier specification will give information about all the types of distortion that we have discussed in order to show how good the amplifier is. The frequency response figure will indicate how closely the amplifier adheres to the same amplification at all frequencies. Sometimes a complete response curve is given and sometimes the specification merely states that the response is within 0.5 db from 20 cycles to 20,000 cycles (or some similar figure). A difference of 0.5 db corresponds with a voltage change of almost 6%, so this means that the amplification will be within 6% of constant through this frequency range.

A distortion figure is also given and, unless otherwise specified, this indicates the amount of harmonic distortion. Unfortunately, it is not usual or convenient to specify what kind of harmonic distortion the figure given may be—entirely second harmonic, third harmonic, or it may be a composite of higher harmonics. This is an unfortunate deficiency of this method of specification.

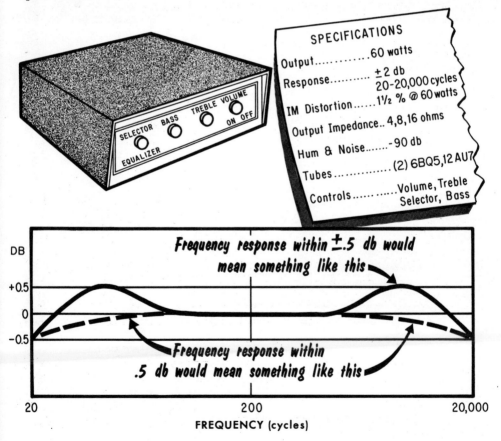

Amplifier Specifications (contd.)

A good modern amplifier might specify a maximum harmonic distortion of 1%. This means that the total of all the harmonic components produced in the amplification of a single sine wave will be less than 1% of the fundamental, and when all of these voltages are squared, added together, and the square root taken, this square root will still not be more than 1% of the fundamental voltage.

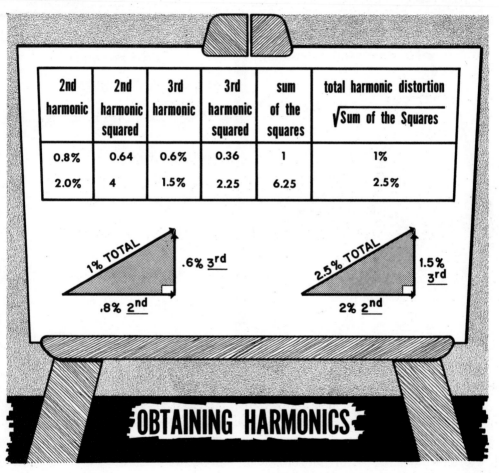

2nd harmonic	2nd harmonic squared	3rd harmonic	3rd harmonic squared	sum of the squares	total harmonic distortion $\sqrt{\text{Sum of the Squares}}$
0.8%	0.64	0.6%	0.36	1	1%
2.0%	4	1.5%	2.25	6.25	2.5%

It is important that, to obtain the total harmonic distortion, one must obtain the square root of the sum of squares of the individual harmonics. The method of combining harmonics is the same regardless of which components are combined. The different components could be second and fifth or any other combination, or a combination of more than just two individual components.

Amplifier Specifications (contd.)

In modern amplifiers in which the harmonic percentage is specified at maximum output, the distortion usually takes the form of clipping on the tops of the waveform, due to the beginning of grid current.

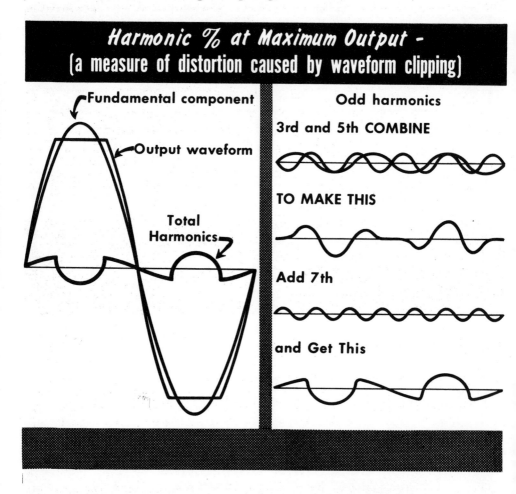

The sharp-peaked distortion component can be analyzed into a series of odd-numbered harmonics, third, fifth, seventh, and so on up the scale. The magnitude of any individual component is quite small compared to the combined peak, as is also the *measured* combined value. The audible effects as well as the visible one seen on an oscilloscope, however, can still be quite noticeable. It has the sound of a knocking at the fundamental frequency, as when the voice coil of the loudspeaker knocks against its end stops. Even a measured 0.5% distortion of this kind is quite readily audible, as well as visible on the waveform displayed by the oscilloscope.

Amplifier Specifications (contd.)

DISTORTION MAY BE SPECIFIED AS INTERMODULATION (IM)

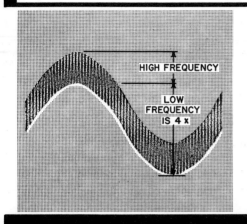
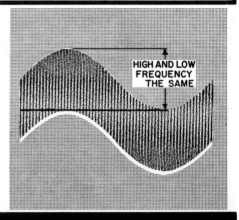

Different possible combination of Amplitude   4:1 or 1:1

and

Differeni combinations of Frequency can be used

40 cps -- 3000 cps
100 cps -- 2000 cps
40 cps -- 2000 cps
60 cps -- 7000 cps, etc

Sometimes the distortion is specified as IM (intermodulation). Unless further information is given about the frequencies used for the test, such a specification is valueless. If the first method of IM test is used, the low frequency (its actual value in cycles per second) is important, as well as the ratio between the *magnitudes* at the two frequencies. The low frequency may be 40 cycles, 60 cycles, or even 100 cycles. Because the handling capacity of an amplifier may be quite different at these three different frequencies, a specification of IM without stating which low frequency was used for the test conveys no real comparison of the performance of different amplifiers.

The peak-to-peak waveform which the amplifier has to handle is the low-frequency voltage *plus* the high-frequency voltage, because one rides atop the other. Consequently the amount of distortion produced will depend upon the ratio between the two voltages, whether this is 4:1, or as is sometimes used, 1:1. Because the results obtained will depend on the precise nature of the curvature or distortion causing them, there is no ready means of converting figures obtained by one test arrangement into figures that would be obtained using the other test arrangement. Consequently the only safe basis for making comparisons between the performance of different amplifiers is to insure that the same combination is used for both tests.

Transient Distortion

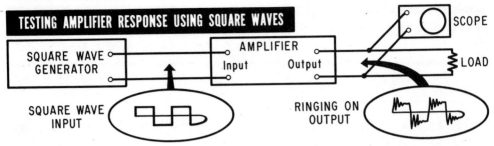

This is still another kind of distortion which can be subdivided into further groups. It is not indicated in the majority of amplifier specifications. An amplifier may have a perfectly flat frequency response throughout the audio range, which should indicate that it will give a faithful reproduction of the input waveform at the output. It may show quite low harmonic distortion and yet when a square wave is amplified, the wave may become considerably distorted by a ringing at the corners of the square.

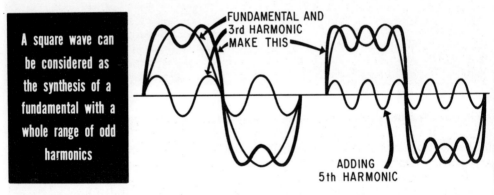

A square wave can be considered as a synthesis or combination of fundamental with a whole range of odd-numbered harmonics. If all these are amplified uniformly, surely the output waveform should still be square? This is true, but it does not take into account possible effects due to time delay in the amplifier, which may not be uniform at all frequencies. Every bit of stray capacitance from a plate or other electrode to ground at different points in the amplifier causes a slight time delay in the amplified audio. This adds up on the way through the amplifier.

If the time delay to all components of the audio waveform is the *same*, the output waveform will still be a square wave, but if it is different for the higher frequency components than it is for the low-frequency fundamental and its lower harmonics, the waveform gets altered. This is one way in which ringing occurs.

DISTORTION

Transient Distortion (contd.)

Another kind of transient distortion occurs when the amplitude of the audio suddenly changes. Suppose that a sine wave is amplified, but is stepped up and down at intervals. This will cause the output waveform to step up and down at intervals, which will cause the output voltage to step up and down. If the amplitude of the sine wave is stepped up and down in such a way that the outline (or *envelope*) follows a square waveform, then the output should faithfully reproduce this.

Many amplifiers are not satisfactory in this regard. When a larger audio voltage is being amplified, the output tubes draw more current, which may alter the bias condition. This means that the supply voltages at different points in the circuit will change. The change will take place according to the time constants of the resistances and capacitances in the supply unit, which may not be the same for all the changing voltages. Consequently the gain of the amplifier may go up and down again or down and up again after a sudden change in the amplitude of the audio. This results in an envelope at the output that is different from the envelope at the input. Unfortunately these effects *can* prove quite severe, even with an amplifier whose specification, using the other methods of test, tells of quite good performance—extremely low distortion and very good frequency response.

Thus amplification is far from being the simple matter we started out by supposing. There are many ways in which an amplifier can distort a composite audio program. Whichever method of specifying these is used, it becomes quite an involved matter to give a statement that is completely satisfactory for comparison purposes.

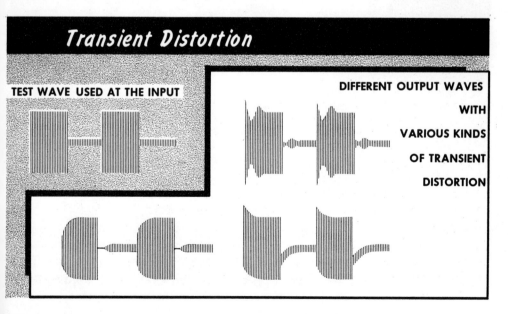

Transient Distortion

TEST WAVE USED AT THE INPUT

DIFFERENT OUTPUT WAVES
WITH
VARIOUS KINDS
OF TRANSIENT
DISTORTION

QUESTIONS AND PROBLEMS

1. Audio transformers are used to produce step-up of voltage or current, to transform impedances to different values, or to make maximum use of available power (as in a loudspeaker). Comment on the relationship among these functions.

2. What are the basic differences between primary inductance and leakage inductance in a transformer?

3. Why is an air gap used in a transformer core? What determines the optimum size of the gap?

4. Can a flat-topped waveform at low frequencies be due to saturation? Comment on the relationship between frequency response, and the limitation imposed by saturation.

5. Would distortion due to saturation be more apparent in an amplifier using triodes or in one using pentodes? Why?

6. What features must be considered in the design of a good audio transformer?

7. Explain how a transformer can help performance (a) at the input to an amplifier, (b) at its output, (c) between tube stages, (d) between transistor stages.

8. What is harmonic distortion? Show how you would identify the presence of different harmonics on the waveform.

9. Explain two methods of measuring harmonic distortion. What would be considered an acceptable figure?

10. What is intermodulation distortion? Describe two different forms it can take.

11. Why are there inconsistencies among the results obtained in different distortion measurements?

12. Write what you would consider to be a good amplifier specification, and comment on the limited validity of any figures you may quote.

13. If a harmonic analysis of a waveform showed 1.6% second, 1.5% third, and 1.2% fifth harmonics, what would you expect the total distortion to be (assuming no higher harmonics are present in measurable quantity)?

14. Comment on the significance of a harmonic measurement when the distortion mainly takes the form of clipping.

15. Comment on the use of square waves for testing (a) as to facts not brought to light that are revealed in other tests, and (b) as to forms of distortion that square-wave testing would not reveal.

16. Discuss some aspects of transient distortion that affect amplifier performance, which are not always included in the specification.

VOL. 2 INDEX

INDEX